SPELLBOUND
A COMPLETE SPELLING PROGRAMME

BOOK A

FOLENS

Introduction To Teachers and Parents

Spellbound is a Complete Spelling Programme for Primary Schools that supplies children with a variety of word lists.

The lists include: Phonics (22 units), Themes (8 units), and High Frequency Words (2 units).

It is recommended that children learn 4 spellings from the word list every night.

The *Spellbound* programme adheres to the objectives advocated by the Revised Primary School Curriculum which state that:

In First and Second Class the child is enabled to:
'spell correctly a range of familiar, important and regularly occurring words…'.

In Third and Fourth Class the child is enabled to:
'use a range of aids and strategies [dictionaries, word lists, word searches, spelling checkers, anagrams, regular word patterns]… to improve his/her command of spelling'.

In Fifth and Sixth Class the child is enabled to:
'observe the conventions of grammar, punctuation and spelling in his/her writing'.

The *Spellbound* series of books follows a specific multi-dimensional programme that assists the child in attaining proficiency in spelling.

This is achieved by:

1. Guiding the child in developing their phonological and phonemic awareness in order that they can readily identify sound and letter patterns within words.

2. Using onset and rime strategies to inculcate an awareness of spelling patterns. This is achieved by introducing word families that share the same 'rime', e.g. Page 56, Book A, the family of 'ay' words.

3. Building up a store of High Frequency Words.

4. Highlighting Commonly Misspelled Words and Homophones.

5. Advocating the use of strategies such as: Predict, Look, Say, Cover, Write, Check.

6. Enabling the children to become familiar with common spelling rules, e.g. the fact that the plural of most words is formed by adding 's'.

The *Spellbound* series of books supplies the child with a systematic and consistent experience of spelling and it is this approach which achieves progress and success.

The books are ostensibly aimed at: Book A: 1st Class, Book B: 2nd Class, Book C: 3rd Class, Book D: 4th Class, Book E: 5th Class and Book F: 6th Class.

Editors:
    Deirdre Whelan, Francis Connolly,
    Sarah Deegan
Cover and Book Design:
    Philip Ryan
Layout:
    Mark McKenna
Illustration:
    Tim Hutchinson
Cover Illustration:
    Tim Hutchinson & Zara Slattery (G.C.I.)

ISBN 978-1-84741-062-7

© Folens Publishers 2008
Hibernian Industrial Estate,
Greenhills Road, Tallaght, Dublin 24
Produced by Folens Publishers.

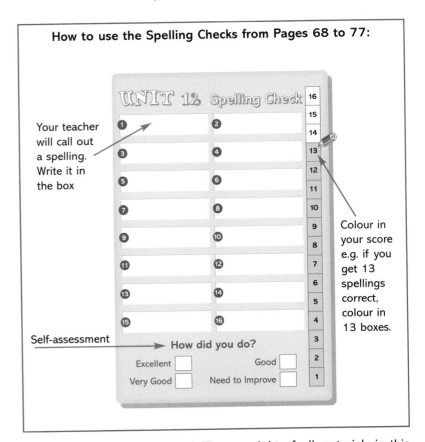

How to use the Spelling Checks from Pages 68 to 77:

UNIT 12 Spelling Check

Your teacher will call out a spelling. Write it in the box

Colour in your score e.g. if you get 13 spellings correct, colour in 13 boxes.

Self-assessment

How did you do?

Excellent ☐   Good ☐
Very Good ☐   Need to Improve ☐

CONTENTS

Unit	Title	Page
Unit 1	**High Frequency Words**	4
Unit 2	Phonics: 'a' words	6
Unit 3	Phonics: 'a' words	8
Unit 4	**High Frequency Words**	10
Unit 5	Phonics: 'i' words	12
Unit 6	Phonics: 'i' words	14
Unit 7	Phonics: 'e' words	16
Unit 8	Phonics: 'o' words	18
Unit 9	Phonics: 'u' words	20
Unit 10	Phonics: 'a' words	22
Unit 11	Phonics: 'i' words	24
Unit 12	Phonics: 'e' words	26
Unit 13	Phonics: 'o' words	28
Unit 14	Phonics: 'u' words	30
Unit 15	Phonics: Magic E with 'a'	32
Unit 16	Phonics: Magic E with i'	34
Unit 17	Phonics: Magic E with 'i'	36
Unit 18	**Theme: The Body**	38
Unit 19	Phonics: Magic E with 'u'	40
Unit 20	**Theme: Clothes**	42
Unit 21	Phonics: Magic E with 'o'	44
Unit 22	**Theme: Farm Animals**	46
Unit 23	Phonics: 'll' endings	48
Unit 24	**Theme: The House**	50
Unit 25	Phonics: 'ck' endings	52
Unit 26	**Theme: Food and Drink**	54
Unit 27	Phonics: 'ay' endings	56
Unit 28	**Theme: Wild Animals**	58
Unit 29	Phonics: 'ar' words	60
Unit 30	**Theme: The Seaside**	62
Unit 31	Phonics: 'ir' and 'or' words	64
Unit 32	**Theme: The Classroom**	66
Spelling Checks		68
Hallowe'en, Christmas, Easter and Summer Checks		76
Complete Word List		78

UNIT 1

Wordlist

❶		❷		❸		❹	
is	in	go	my	the	red	for	big
it	to	me	see	run	not	can	and

A. Write the missing letters.

1. i s
2. __ t
3. i __
4. t __

5. g __
6. __ e
7. m __
8. s __ __

9. t __ e
10. r __ n
11. re __
12. n __ __

13. f __ __
14. __ an
15. b __ __
16. a __ d

B. Unscramble these words. Write them. Find them in the wordsearch.

1. nad __and__
2. urn _____
3. orf _____
4. hte _____
5. anc _____
6. ibg _____

```
y  a  l (a  n  d) v  h
j  w  h  f  o  d  a  n
r  r  f  o  r  a  n  t
u  s  a  t  a  c  a  v
n  s  m  h  m  t  o  h
a  b  h  e  w  r  u  j
b  i  g  a  n  d  g  m
m  a  n  e  c  a  n  j
```

C. Find 8 words in the caterpillar. Write them.

the see can me red big go run

1. the
2. _____
3. _____
4. _____
5. _____
6. _____
7. _____
8. _____

D. Write the missing words. Use the word list.

1. There are grey squirrels and __red__ squirrels.
2. Jack _____ Jill went up the hill.
3. Run, _____ as fast as you can!
4. I _____ see a cat.

Colour the words. Use the correct colours.

and
red

not
green

big
yellow

the
blue

see
orange

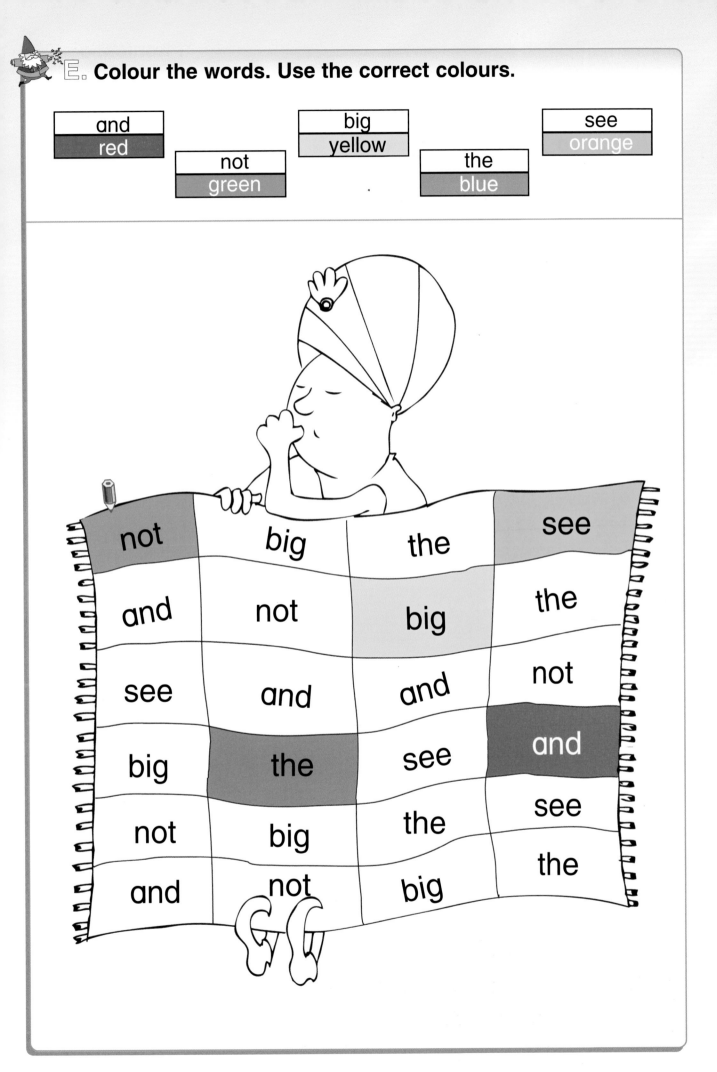

UNIT 2

Word List

①		②		③		④	
pan	van	hat	sat	tap	rap	rag	mad
ran	has	rat	pat	map	ham	sad	had

A. Write the missing letters.

1. p _a_ n
2. ra __
3. v __ __
4. h __ s
5. ha __
6. r __ __
7. s __ t
8. pa __
9. t __ p
10. ma __
11. r __ __
12. h __ m
13. r __ __
14. sa __
15. m __ d
16. __ a __

B. Colour the correct spelling.

1.	sda	sad

2.	van	ven

3.	has	haz

4.	rap	rpa

5.	madd	mad

6.	pon	pan

C. Match and write.

ha — an
h   p
p   t
ta   as
h   d
ma   am

1. <u>hat</u>
2. _____
3. _____
4. _____
5. _____
6. _____

D. Write the word. Colour the pictures.

1. ___van___   2. _____   3. _____   4. _____

E. Find 8 words in the caterpillar. Write them.

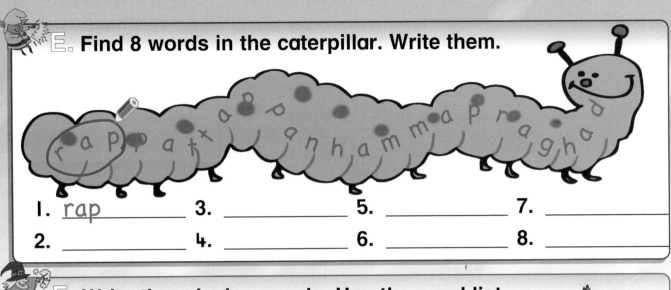

1. rap   3. _____   5. _____   7. _____

2. _____   4. _____   6. _____   8. _____

F. Write the missing words. Use the word list.

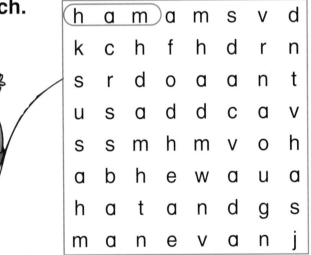

1. My dad fried an egg in the pan _____.

2. The wind blew my _____ off my head.

3. I _____ after the ball.

4. Ben has a _____ roll for his lunch.

G. Unscramble these words. Write them.
Find them in the wordsearch.

1. ahm   ham

2. asd   _____

3. dha   _____

4. ahs   _____

5. tha   _____

6. nva   _____

h	a	m	a	m	s	v	d
k	c	h	f	h	d	r	n
s	r	d	o	a	a	n	t
u	s	a	d	d	c	a	v
s	s	m	h	m	v	o	h
a	b	h	e	w	a	u	a
h	a	t	a	n	d	g	s
m	a	n	e	v	a	n	j

H. Colour the words that begin with 'h'.

pan   sad   rap   map   mad

ran   rag   had   tap

van   has   hat   ham   rat   sat   pat

UNIT 3

Word List

lap ❶	cap	bat ❷	fat	jam ❸	bad	can ❹	tan
nap	gap	mat	bag	dam	dad	fan	man

A. Write the missing letters.

1. l _a_ p
2. n __ __
3. ca __
4. g __ p

5. ba __
6. m __ __
7. f __ t
8. b __ __

9. j __ __
10. da __
11. b __ d
12. da __

13. c __ n
14. fa __
15. t __ __
16. m __ n

B. Colour the correct spelling.

1.	mann	man
2.	fat	fta
3.	gam	jam

4.	kan	can
5.	bam	dam
6.	fon	fan

C. Match and write.

n   at
b   m
c   am
fa   an
ja   t
d   ap

1. _nap_
2. _____
3. _____
4. _____
5. _____
6. _____

D. Write the word. Colour the pictures.

1. ___dam___
2. _____
3. _____
4. _____

E. Find 8 words in the caterpillar. Write them.

1. ___cap___ 3. _____ 5. _____ 7. _____

2. _____ 4. _____ 6. _____ 8. _____

F. Write the missing words. Use the word list.

1. Our cat likes to sit on my ___lap___.

2. My _____ is taller than my mum.

3. My baby sister goes for a _____ in her cot.

4. I love strawberry _____.

G. Unscramble these words. Write them. Find them in the wordsearch.

1. amn   ___man___

2. abd   _____

3. aft   _____

4. pga   _____

5. abg   _____

6. pla   _____

d	s	n	m	a	n	v	d
b	c	q	g	a	p	r	n
a	f	d	o	a	y	n	w
d	e	a	b	d	v	a	c
r	j	l	a	m	l	o	t
a	b	h	g	w	a	u	a
f	a	b	a	n	p	g	s
z	t	n	f	a	t	r	j

H. Colour the words that end in 'an'.

cap

can

mat

bad

tan

lap

man

fan

bag

jam

*** 9 ***

UNIT 4

Word List

①		②		③		④	
up	am	be	he	on	get	but	all
we	at	do	no	got	did	you	are

A. Write the missing letters.

1. u <u>p</u>
2. __ e
3. a __
4. __ t

5. b __
6. __ o
7. h __
8. __ o

9. o __
10. g __ t
11. __ e __
12. d __ d

13. bu __
14. y __ __
15. __ ll
16. a __ e

B. Unscramble these words. Write them. Find them in the wordsearch.

1. oyu   <u>you</u>

2. ogt   _____

3. lal   _____

4. rae   _____

5. tge   _____

6. ddi   _____

x	j	m	d	i	d	k	r
m	a	e	c	b	r	e	u
d	p	q	m	n	j	p	g
t	y	o	u	a	r	e	g
q	j	w	d	h	x	i	x
z	a	n	h	b	l	r	e
a	l	l	g	o	t	m	q
r	q	s	g	e	t	k	k

C. Find 8 words in the caterpillar. Write them.

youuonnoareallgetdiddo

1. <u>you</u>
2. _____
3. _____
4. _____
5. _____
6. _____
7. _____
8. _____

D. Write the missing words. Use the word list.

1. We are <u>all</u> going to the zoo.

2. My dog is _____ home.

3. I _____ six years old.

4. The cat is _____ the swing.

*** 10 ***

Colour the words. Use the correct colours.

Word List

①		②		③		④	
fix	hit	dip	pig	big	him	hid	fin
fit	bit	hip	dig	mix	his	did	bin

A. Write the missing letters.

1. f _i_ x
2. fi __
3. h __ t
4. b __ __
5. d __ p
6. hi __
7. p __ g
8. __ ig
9. bi __
10. __ ix
11. h __ m
12. hi __
13. h __ d
14. d __ d
15. f __ n
16. bi __

B. Colour the correct spelling.

1. | himm | him |

2. | pig | pgi |

3. | fit | tif |

4. | finn | fin |

5. | bgi | big |

6. | bit | bitt |

C. Match and write.

f   m
d   ig
fi   ix
hi   d
di   ip
h   n

1. fix
2. _____
3. _____
4. _____
5. _____
6. _____

D. Write the word. Colour the pictures.

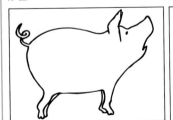  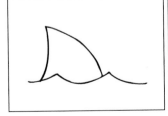 

1. ___pig___
2. _____
3. _____
4. _____

E. Find 8 words in the caterpillar. Write them.

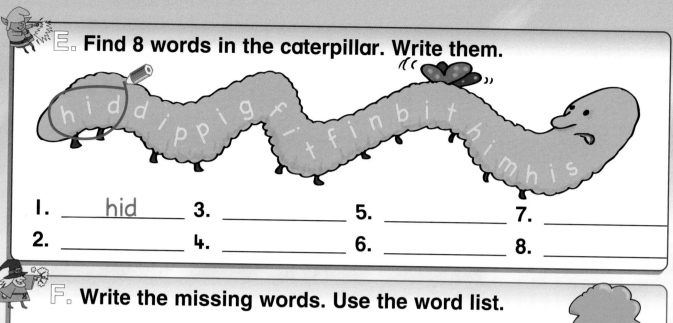

1. ___hid___   3. _____   5. _____   7. _____

2. _____   4. _____   6. _____   8. _____

F. Write the missing words. Use the word list.

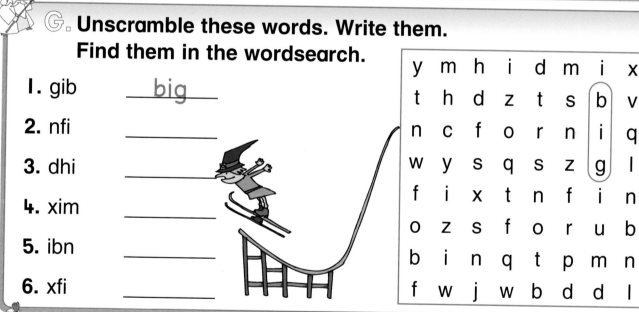

1. A baby ___pig___ is called a piglet.

2. I _____ my homework when I went home.

3. Our dog _____ his bone under a tree.

4. I asked Tim for a loan of _____ pencil.

G. Unscramble these words. Write them. Find them in the wordsearch.

1. gib   ___big___

2. nfi   _____

3. dhi   _____

4. xim   _____

5. ibn   _____

6. xfi   _____

y	m	h	i	d	m	i	x
t	h	d	z	t	s	b	v
n	c	f	o	r	n	i	q
w	y	s	q	s	z	g	l
f	i	x	t	n	f	i	n
o	z	s	f	o	r	u	b
b	i	n	q	t	p	m	n
f	w	j	w	b	d	d	l

H. Colour the words that begin with 'h'.

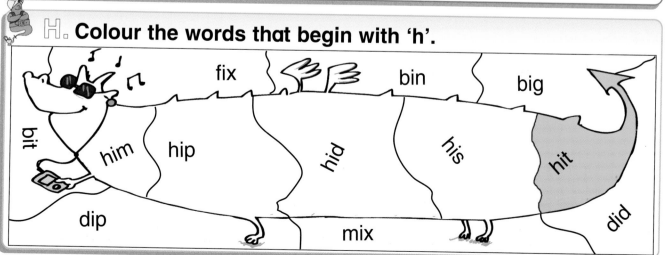

fix   bin   big

bit   him   hip   hid   his   hit

dip   mix   did

Word List

①		②		③		④	
kid	sit	lit	tin	rib	rip	pip	wig
lid	pit	win	pin	bib	lip	tip	six

A. Write the missing letters.

1. k __ d
2. l __ __
3. si __
4. p __ t
5. l __ t
6. w __ __
7. ti __
8. p __ __
9. r __ b
10. b __ b
11. ri __
12. l __ __
13. p __ p
14. ti __
15. w __ __
16. si __

B. Colour the correct spelling.

1. | sicks | six |
2. | weg | wig |
3. | tipe | tip |

4. | lep | lip |
5. | sit | sut |
6. | kid | cid |

C. Match and write.

k   ig
w   ix
li   id
s   ip
wi   t
r   n

1. _____
2. _____
3. _____
4. _____
5. _____
6. _____

D. Write the word. Colour the pictures.

1. _____ 2. _____ 3. _____ 4. _____

E. Find 8 words in the caterpillar. Write them.

s i t t i p p i t t i n w i n l i p p i p k i d

1. _____   3. _____   5. _____   7. _____

2. _____   4. _____   6. _____   8. _____

F. Write the missing words. Use the word list.

1. The dog had _____ puppies.

2. A baby goat is called a _____.

3. I put the _____ on the pot.

4. My baby brother wears a _____.

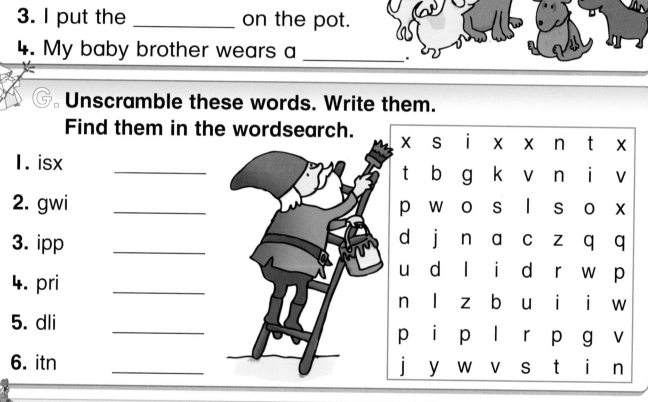

G. Unscramble these words. Write them. Find them in the wordsearch.

1. isx _____

2. gwi _____

3. ipp _____

4. pri _____

5. dli _____

6. itn _____

x	s	i	x	x	n	t	x
t	b	g	k	v	n	i	v
p	w	o	s	l	s	o	x
d	j	n	a	c	z	q	q
u	d	l	i	d	r	w	p
n	l	z	b	u	i	i	w
p	i	p	l	r	p	g	v
j	y	w	v	s	t	i	n

H. Colour the words that end in 'ip'.

kid   lid   bib   wig

pip   rib   win

tip   rip

pin   lip

pit   lit   tin

Word List

①	②	③	④
ten den	pet wet	get red	bed web
men hen	vet jet	net fed	leg yes

A. Write the missing letters.

1. t __ n
2. me __
3. __ __ n
4. h __ n

5. p __ __
6. ve __
7. w __ t
8. je __

9. ge __
10. n __ __
11. re __
12. f __ d

13. b __ d
14. le __
15. w __ __
16. ye __

B. Colour the correct spelling.

1. | lge | leg |

2. | web | wob |

3. | hen | hun |

4. | get | gat |

5. | tne | ten |

6. | vet | vot |

C. Match and write.

b — es
t — eb
y — ed
w — en
je — eg
l — t

1. _____
2. _____
3. _____
4. _____
5. _____
6. _____

D. Write the word. Colour the pictures.

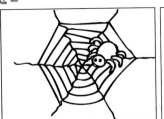

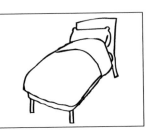

1. _____   2. _____   3. _____   4. _____

E. Find 8 words in the caterpillar. Write them.

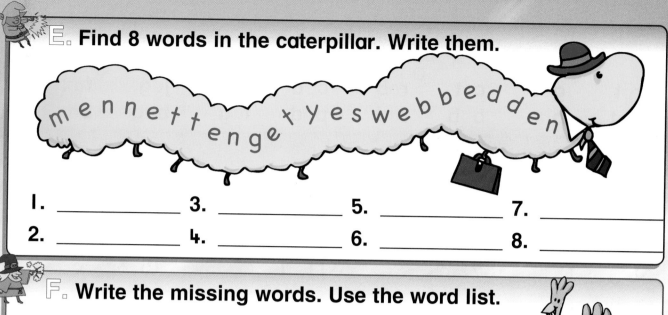

1. _____   3. _____   5. _____   7. _____

2. _____   4. _____   6. _____   8. _____

F. Write the missing words. Use the word list.

1. I went to _____ early last night.

2. The _____ laid two eggs.

3. The spider made a _____.

4. When I grow up I want to be a _____.

G. Unscramble these words. Write them. Find them in the wordsearch.

1. egl _____

2. eys _____

3. bwe _____

4. twe _____

5. edn _____

6. tve _____

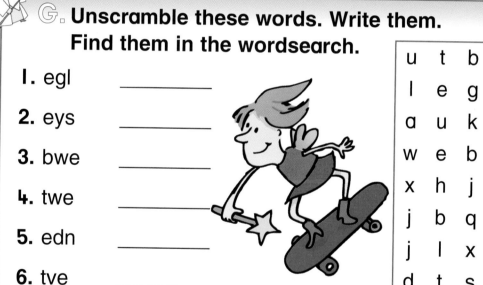

u	t	b	w	e	t	g	v
l	e	g	x	e	v	g	e
a	u	k	e	o	d	c	t
w	e	b	a	p	y	e	s
x	h	j	k	v	r	d	j
j	b	q	m	z	p	e	t
j	l	x	f	b	p	n	j
d	t	s	a	q	a	k	z

H. Colour the words that end in 'et'.

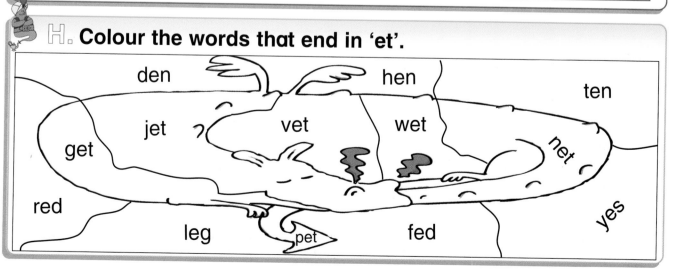

den   hen   ten

jet   vet   wet   net

get

red   yes

leg   pet   fed

Word List

①	②	③	④
rot got	cot rob	cod dog	jog fox
dot pot	bob rod	pod fog	bog box

A. Write the missing letters.

1. r __ t
2. do__
3. g __ t
4. po __

5. c __ t
6. __ ob
7. ro __
8. r __ d

9. __ od
10. p __ d
11. d __ __
12. fo __

13. j __ g
14. __ __ g
15. f __ x
16. __ o__

B. Colour the correct spelling.

1.

fxo	fox

2.

bog	bgo

3.

doc	cod

4.

box	bux

5.

pot	pto

6.

cit	cot

C. Match and write.

f   g
ro   t
jo   ox
co   t
d   od
r   og

1. _____
2. _____
3. _____
4. _____
5. _____
6. _____

D. Write the word. Colour the pictures.

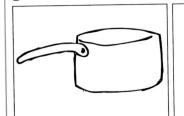   

1. _____ 2. _____ 3. _____ 4. _____

E. Find 8 words in the caterpillar. Write them.

foxfoggotrotpoddogboxcot

1. _____   3. _____   5. _____   7. _____
2. _____   4. _____   6. _____   8. _____

F. Write the missing words. Use the word list.

1. The baby is in the _____.

2. I like _____ for my tea.

3. The _____ has a bushy tail.

4. I have a small, black _____.

G. Unscramble these words. Write them.
Find them in the wordsearch.

1. oxf   _____

2. gjo   _____

3. ogb   _____

4. fgo   _____

5. cdo   _____

6. cto   _____

b	j	i	s	g	p	t	h
c	o	t	b	o	g	z	j
f	o	g	o	r	f	k	o
s	u	y	n	z	b	c	g
h	d	z	w	y	h	o	x
p	r	q	c	h	m	d	w
c	k	w	f	o	x	q	k
m	y	s	m	u	l	p	k

H. Colour the words that end in 'ot'.

rod   bob   fox   dog
rot   cot
pod   dot   got   pot
    cod   fog   box

19

UNIT 9

Word List

①		②		③		④	
nut	put	fun	sun	rug	hug	tug	cup
but	hut	bun	gun	dug	mug	mud	cut

A. Write the missing letters.

1. n __ t
2. b __ __
3. pu __
4. __ ut

5. f __ n
6. bu __
7. __ un
8. gu __

9. r __ g
10. d __ g
11. h __ g
12. mu __

13. tu __
14. m __ d
15. c __ p
16. __ ut

B. Colour the correct spelling.

1.	guh	hug

2.	hut	tuh

3.	mud	mdu

4.	dug	dgut

5.	fum	fun

6.	cut	ctu

C. Match and write.

n   t
bu   d
mu   n
su   ut
f   up
c   un

1. _____
2. _____
3. _____
4. _____
5. _____
6. _____

D. Write the word. Colour the pictures.

 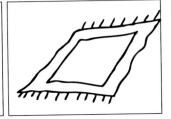  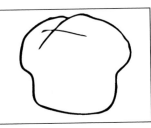

1. _____
2. _____
3. _____
4. _____

E. Find 8 words in the caterpillar. Write them.

c u p c u t r u g d u g f u n b u n n u t b u t

1. _____   3. _____   5. _____   7. _____

2. _____   4. _____   6. _____   8. _____

F. Write the missing words. Use the word list.

1. My dog fell into the _____.

2. I _____ the paper in the bin.

3. We had _____ in the park.

4. The squirrel is eating a _____.

G. Unscramble these words. Write them.
   Find them in the wordsearch.

1. upc   _____

2. gmu   _____

3. nus   _____

4. ufn   _____

5. nbu   _____

6. upt   _____

p	u	t	h	k	z	q	v
z	c	u	p	p	m	r	u
o	v	b	u	n	l	d	o
q	t	d	e	m	u	g	s
b	g	w	x	y	z	j	u
z	b	b	x	n	w	h	n
a	y	t	l	z	t	i	w
f	j	t	w	l	f	u	n

H. Colour the words that end in 'ug'.

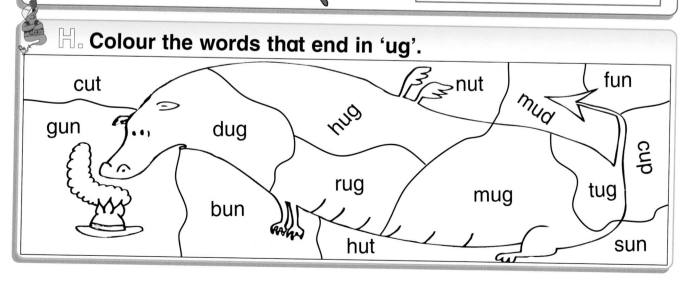

cut   nut   fun

gun   dug   hug   mud   cup

rug   mug   tug

bun

hut   sun

UNIT 10

Word List

①	②	③	④
wag stag	clap flap	chat plan	that have
flag drag	trap ram	flat than	ant glad

A. Write the missing letters.

1. w __ g
2. fl __ __
3. s __ a __
4. dr __ __

5. c __ a __
6. tr __ __
7. __ lap
8. r __ __

9. ch __ __
10. f __ a __
11. pl __ __
12. t __ a __

13. th __ __
14. a __ t
15. h __ v __
16. gl __ d

B. Colour the correct spelling.

1.	taht	that

4.	chat	caht

2.	flap	flup

5.	stga	stag

3.	thun	than

6.	plan	plon

C. Match and write.

ch   ag
st   an
pl   at
gl   ap
tr   ad
a   nt

1. _____
2. _____
3. _____
4. _____
5. _____
6. _____

D. Write the word. Colour the pictures.

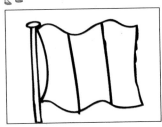

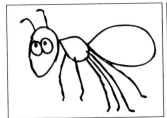

1. _____ 2. _____ 3. _____ 4. _____

E. Find 8 words in the caterpillar. Write them.

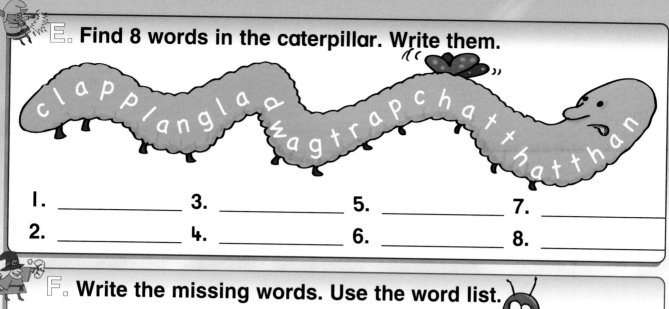

1. _____ 3. _____ 5. _____ 7. _____

2. _____ 4. _____ 6. _____ 8. _____

F. Write the missing words. Use the word list.

1. An _____ has six legs.

2. The dog began to _____ his tail.

3. The daddy deer is called a _____.

4. I am taller _____ my sister.

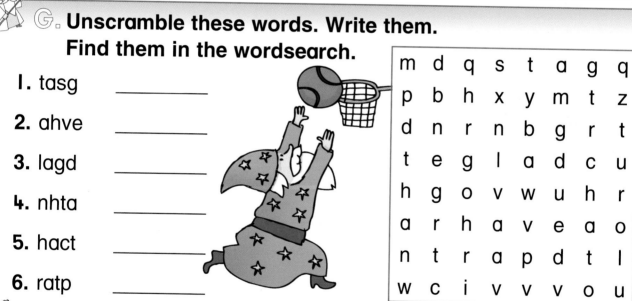

G. Unscramble these words. Write them. Find them in the wordsearch.

1. tasg _____

2. ahve _____

3. lagd _____

4. nhta _____

5. hact _____

6. ratp _____

m	d	q	s	t	a	g	q
p	b	h	x	y	m	t	z
d	n	r	n	b	g	r	t
t	e	g	l	a	d	c	u
h	g	o	v	w	u	h	r
a	r	h	a	v	e	a	o
n	t	r	a	p	d	t	l
w	c	i	v	v	v	o	u

H. Colour the words that end in 'ag'.

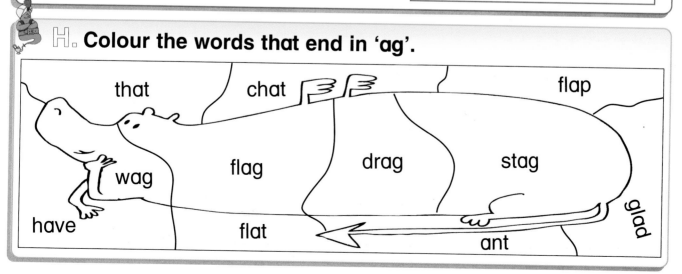

that   chat   flap

wag   flag   drag   stag

have   flat   ant   glad

Word List

❶	❷	❸	❹
zip ship	trip miss	ink think	still twig
whip skip	with kiss	pink this	milk slid

A. Write the missing letters.

1. z __ p
2. wh __ p
3. s __ i __
4. sk __ __

5. t __ i __
6. wi __ h
7. m __ ss
8. ki __ __

9. i __ __
10. pi __ __
11. t __ in __
12. th __ __

13. st __ ll
14. m __ l __
15. tw __ __
16. __ __ id

B. Colour the correct spelling.

1. | wiht | with |

2. | pink | pikn |

3. | mikl | milk |

4. | still | stil |

5. | tink | think |

6. | thes | this |

C. Match and write.

sh   lk
mi   ig
tw   ip
sl   th
wi   ill
st   id

1. _____
2. _____
3. _____
4. _____
5. _____
6. _____

D. Write the word. Colour the pictures.

  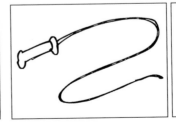 

1. _____   2. _____   3. _____   4. _____

E. Find 8 words in the caterpillar. Write them.

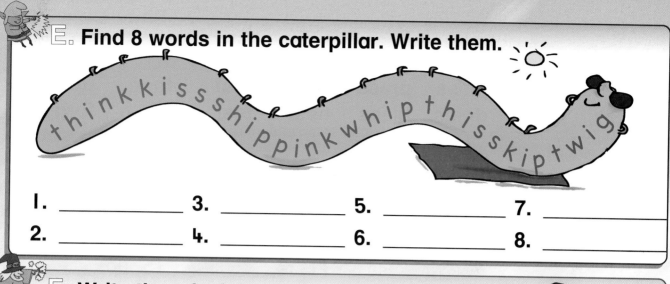

1. _____   3. _____   5. _____   7. _____

2. _____   4. _____   6. _____   8. _____

F. Write the missing words. Use the word list.

1. I know how to _____.

2. We went on a _____ to the zoo.

3. The cow gives us _____.

4. I went to the park _____ my mum.

G. Unscramble these words. Write them.
Find them in the wordsearch.

1. npik   _____

2. hits   _____

3. lsitl   _____

4. hitnk   _____

5. twih   _____

6. witg   _____

p	t	f	t	h	i	n	k
i	w	i	c	r	s	g	u
n	i	s	t	i	l	l	w
k	g	l	p	u	k	q	i
v	t	o	w	y	q	s	t
q	p	k	n	s	e	g	h
z	m	x	g	m	s	n	j
t	h	i	s	z	o	q	r

H. Colour the words that begin with 't'.

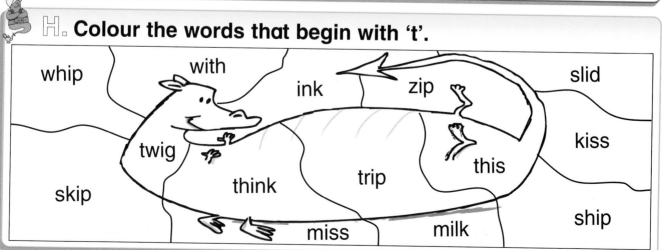

whip   with   ink   zip   slid
twig   think   trip   this   kiss
skip   miss   milk   ship

Word List

set	peg	mess	press	best	rest	then	upset
met	less	dress	bless	nest	test	when	forget

A. Write the missing letters.

1. s __ t
2. __ et
3. p__ g
4. le__ __

5. __ __ ss
6. d __ e __ s
7. __ r __ ss
8. bl __ ss

9. b __ st
10. __ e __ t
11. re__ __
12. __ e__ t

13. th __ n
14. w__ e__
15. up __ __ __
16. __ __ rget

B. Colour the correct spelling.

1.	rets	rest

2.	forget	fourget

3.	whin	when

4.	dres	dress

5.	upset	upste

6.	ntse	nest

C. Match and write.

p   get
th   ess
for   en
n   eg
dr   set
up   est

1. _____
2. _____
3. _____
4. _____
5. _____
6. _____

D. Write the word. Colour the pictures.

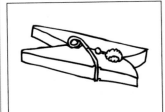

1. _____
2. _____
3. _____
4. _____

E. Find 8 words in the caterpillar. Write them.

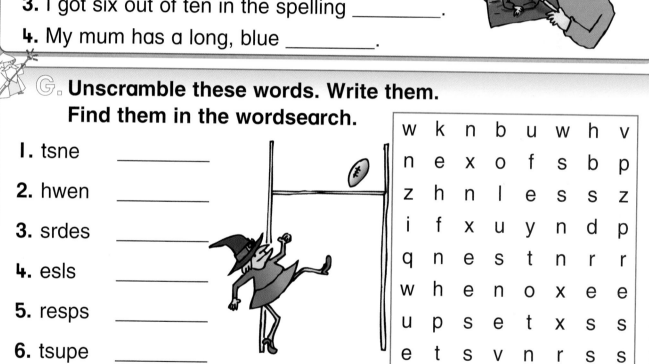

resttthenmessssetpegnestforgetupset

1. _____   3. _____   5. _____   7. _____

2. _____   4. _____   6. _____   8. _____

F. Write the missing words. Use the word list.

1. I ate one sweet and kept the _____.

2. Ben is the _____ in the class at Art.

3. I got six out of ten in the spelling _____.

4. My mum has a long, blue _____.

G. Unscramble these words. Write them. Find them in the wordsearch.

1. tsne   _____

2. hwen   _____

3. srdes   _____

4. esls   _____

5. resps   _____

6. tsupe   _____

w	k	n	b	u	w	h	v
n	e	x	o	f	s	b	p
z	h	n	l	e	s	s	z
i	f	x	u	y	n	d	p
q	n	e	s	t	n	r	r
w	h	e	n	o	x	e	e
u	p	s	e	t	x	s	s
e	t	s	v	n	r	s	s

H. Colour the words that end in 'ess'.

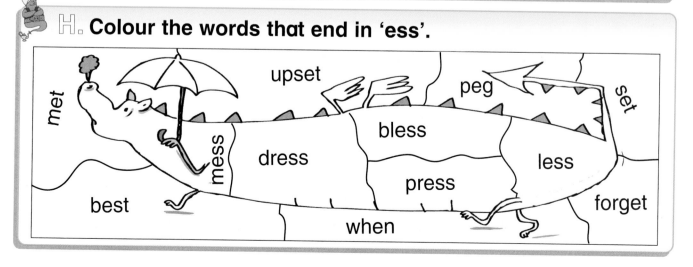

met   upset   peg   set   mess   bless   less   dress   press   best   when   forget

Word List

| on | hot | ① | log | moss | ② | top | shot | ③ | shop | flop | ④ |
| not | lot | | blob | toss | | mop | trot | | stop | drop | |

A. Write the missing letters.

1. __ n

2. n __ t

3. __ ot

4. l __ __

5. l __ g

6. b __ o __

7. mo __ __

8. __ __ ss

9. t __ p

10. m __ __

11. s __ o __

12. tr __ __

13. sh __ p

14. __ t __ p

15. fl __ __

16. d __ o __

B. Colour the correct spelling.

1.	tos	toss
2.	lug	log
3.	shot	shet

4.	folp	flop
5.	stop	sopt
6.	dpor	drop

C. Match and write.

l   hot

flo   n

m   og

o   ss

s   op

mo   p

1. _____

2. _____

3. _____

4. _____

5. _____

6. _____

D. Write the word. Colour the pictures.

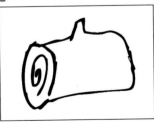 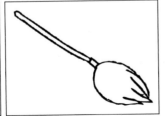  

1. _____   2. _____   3. _____   4. _____

E. Find 8 words in the caterpillar. Write them.

shopmopnotonlogshottopmoss

1. _____ 3. _____ 5. _____ 7. _____

2. _____ 4. _____ 6. _____ 8. _____

F. Write the missing words. Use the word list.

1. Mum put a _____ on the fire.

2. I put a _____ of paint on my picture.

3. I have a _____ of books.

4. The horse began to _____.

G. Unscramble these words. Write them. Find them in the wordsearch.

1. soms   _____

2. plfo   _____

3. prdo   _____

4. hsop   _____

5. lobb   _____

6. tsoh   _____

m	o	v	c	b	l	o	b
n	z	d	v	q	r	l	h
s	j	h	t	v	l	e	s
j	m	o	s	s	f	d	h
b	p	b	u	j	l	d	o
e	s	h	o	t	o	r	p
u	j	q	m	l	p	o	t
t	x	b	m	w	v	p	e

H. Colour the words that end in 'op'.

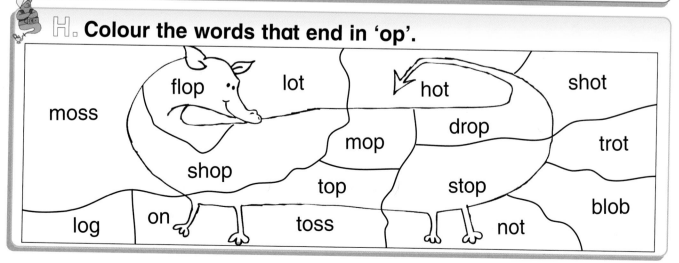

moss   flop   lot   hot   shot   drop   mop   trot   shop   top   stop   blob   log   on   toss   not

Word List

	①		②		③		④
rub	run	jug	plug	dust	trust	bud	shut
tub	nun	bug	slug	rust	bus	sum	club

A. Write the missing letters.

1. r __ b
2. t __ __
3. __ un
4. n __ n

5. j __ __
6. __ ug
7. p __ u __
8. sl __ __

9. du __ __
10. r __ st
11. t __ u __ t
12. b __ __

13. __ ud
14. s __ m
15. sh __ t
16. c __ u __

B. Colour the correct spelling.

1.	shet	shut
2.	sume	sum
3.	dost	dust

4.	ruts	rust
5.	trust	truts
6.	sugl	slug

C. Match and write.

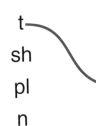

t   ug
sh   lub
pl   ub
n   ust
c   ut
d   un

1. _____
2. _____
3. _____
4. _____
5. _____
6. _____

D. Write the word. Colour the pictures.

1. _____
2. _____
3. _____
4. _____

E. Find 8 words in the caterpillar. Write them.

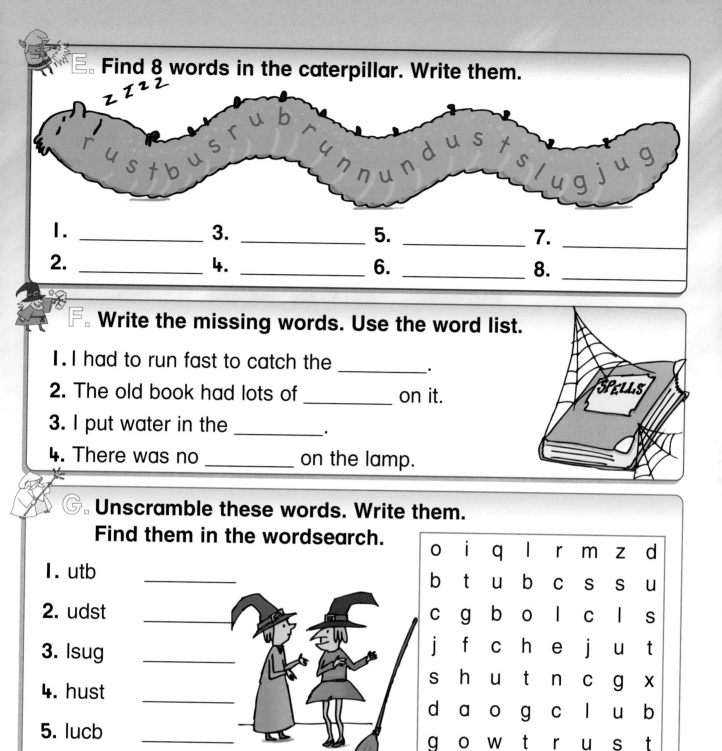

1. _____
2. _____
3. _____
4. _____
5. _____
6. _____
7. _____
8. _____

F. Write the missing words. Use the word list.

1. I had to run fast to catch the _____.
2. The old book had lots of _____ on it.
3. I put water in the _____.
4. There was no _____ on the lamp.

G. Unscramble these words. Write them. Find them in the wordsearch.

1. utb   _____
2. udst   _____
3. lsug   _____
4. hust   _____
5. lucb   _____
6. rutst   _____

o	i	q	l	r	m	z	d
b	t	u	b	c	s	s	u
c	g	b	o	l	c	l	s
j	f	c	h	e	j	u	t
s	h	u	t	n	c	g	x
d	a	o	g	c	l	u	b
g	o	w	t	r	u	s	t
z	k	r	k	c	q	r	p

H. Colour the words that begin with 'r'.

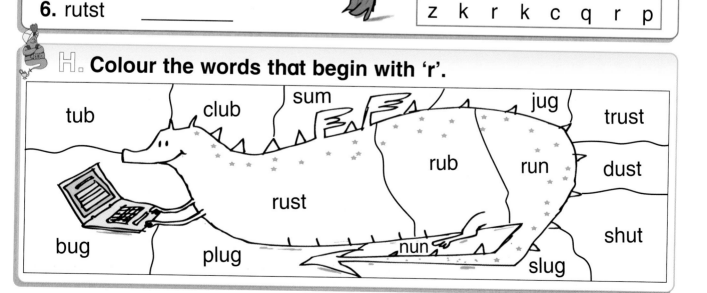

tub   club   sum   jug   trust

rub   run   dust

rust

bug   plug   nun   slug   shut

UNIT 15

Word List

①	②	③	④
cake take	late date	same case	cane mane
rake care	gate fade	name made	lane face

A. Write the missing letters.

1. cak __
2. r __ k __
3. ta __ __
4. c __ re

5. l __ t __
6. ga __ __
7. d __ te
8. f __ de

9. sa __ __
10. n __ me
11. ca __ __
12. m __ d __

13. ca __ __
14. __ __ ne
15. man __
16. f __ c __

B. Colour the correct spelling.

1.	mena	mane

2.	cake	caek

3.	name	neme

4.	layn	lane

5.	take	tace

6.	geat	gate

C. Match and write.

na   ne
ma   e
f   te
m   me
rak   ace
la   ade

1. _____
2. _____
3. _____
4. _____
5. _____
6. _____

D. Write the word. Colour the pictures.

1. _____
2. _____
3. _____
4. _____

E. Find 8 words in the caterpillar. Write them.

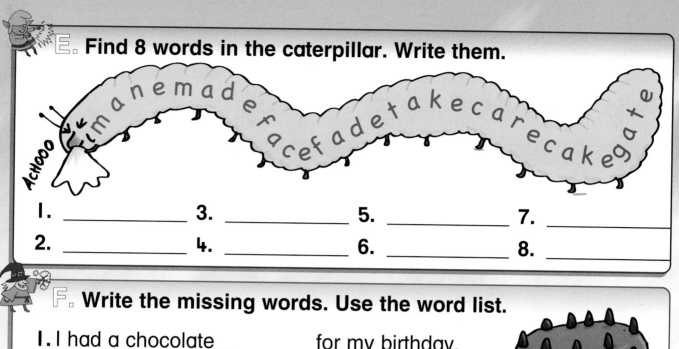

1. _____   3. _____   5. _____   7. _____

2. _____   4. _____   6. _____   8. _____

F. Write the missing words. Use the word list.

1. I had a chocolate _____ for my birthday.

2. A horse has a _____.

3. My _____ is Kate.

4. I have the _____ colour eyes as my sister.

G. Unscramble these words. Write them.
   Find them in the wordsearch.

1. afce   _____

2. nema   _____

3. aesm   _____

4. teda   _____

5. anle   _____

6. krae   _____

z	l	e	f	a	c	e	x
f	a	t	l	o	w	k	a
d	n	l	k	t	w	d	n
a	e	r	l	l	k	a	a
r	v	s	a	m	e	t	m
a	c	m	a	n	e	e	e
k	p	k	g	c	u	n	k
e	n	q	h	v	r	l	j

H. Colour the words that begin with 'c'

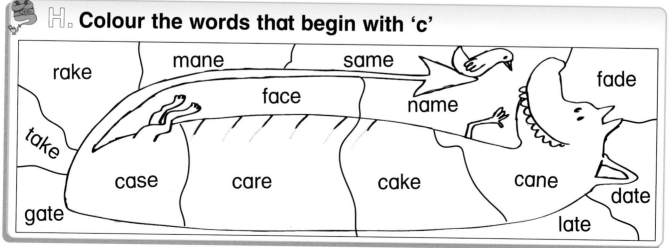

rake   mane   same   fade

face   name

take

case   care   cake   cane

gate   late   date

Word List

① file	pile	② pipe	ride	③ wine	bite	④ hide	like
mile	tile	ripe	tide	fine	kite	pine	time

A. Write the missing letters.

1. fi __ __
2. m __ le
3. p __ le
4. ti __ __

5. p __ pe
6. __ ipe
7. r __ de
8. __ ide

9. win __
10. fi __ __
11. __ ite
12. ki __ __

13. h __ de
14. pin __
15. li __ __
16. __ ime

B. Colour the correct spelling.

1.	riep	ripe

4.	pile	pil

2.	like	lik

5.	fiel	file

3.	kiet	kite

6.	wine	weni

C. Match and write.

pin — ike
m — ne
l — pe
wi — e
ti — ile
ri — me

1. _____
2. _____
3. _____
4. _____
5. _____
6. _____

D. Write the word. Colour the pictures.

 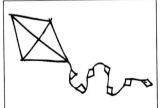  

1. _____
2. _____
3. _____
4. _____

E. Find 8 words in the caterpillar. Write them.

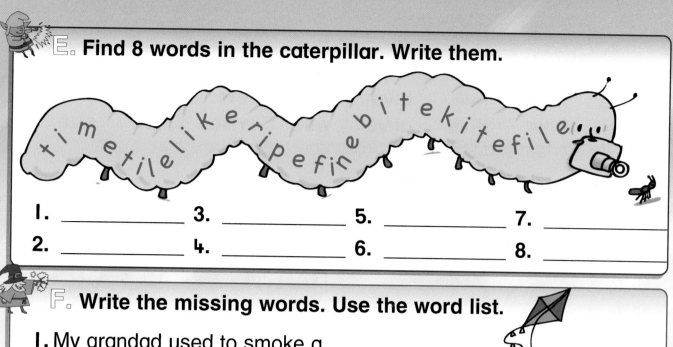

1. _____   3. _____   5. _____   7. _____

2. _____   4. _____   6. _____   8. _____

F. Write the missing words. Use the word list.

1. My grandad used to smoke a _____.

2. I love flying my _____ at the beach.

3. The _____ tree is used as a Christmas tree.

4. I took a bite out of the _____ apple.

G. Unscramble these words. Write them.
Find them in the wordsearch.

1. itke   _____

2. mtie   _____

3. inwe   _____

4. prie   _____

5. dehi   _____

6. ielk   _____

a	y	w	w	j	t	i	k
q	r	n	m	z	i	a	o
x	k	n	v	n	m	h	d
q	k	i	t	e	e	i	z
r	i	p	e	o	l	d	w
s	o	l	h	j	e	e	c
l	i	k	e	w	z	z	a
r	p	c	w	i	n	e	s

H. Colour the words that end in 'ile'

pine   pile   bite   like   hide   time   ripe

file   tile   mile   tide

kite   fine   wine   ride   pipe

Phonics: Magic E with 'i'

Word List

❶		❷		❸		❹	
wide	hike	five	hive	fire	hire	wife	smile
side	bike	dive	alive	wire	wise	life	size

A. Write the missing letters.

1. wi __ __   5. fi __ __   9. f __ re   13. w __ fe

2. s __ de   6. d __ ve   10. wi __ __   14. __ if __

3. hi __ __   7. hi __ __   11. __ ire   15. s __ i __ __

4. b __ ke   8. a __ ive   12. wi __ __   16. __ iz __

B. Colour the correct spelling.

1. | fier | fire |

2. | bike | bice |

3. | sied | side |

4. | lief | life |

5. | smile | simle |

6. | ailve | alive |

C. Match and write.

w   ze   1. _____

a   ife   2. _____

si   live   3. _____

bi   re   4. _____

hi   ile   5. _____

sm   ke   6. _____

D. Write the word. Colour the pictures.

1. _____   2. _____   3. _____   4. _____

E. Find 8 words in the caterpillar. Write them.

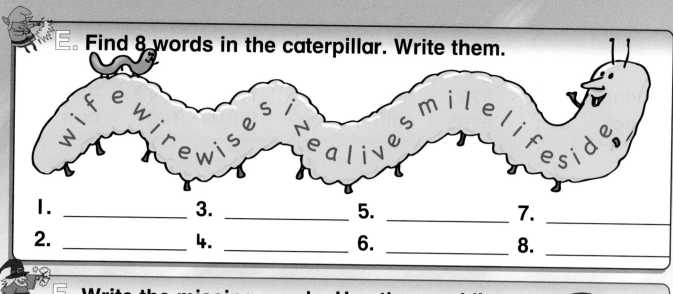

1. _____   3. _____   5. _____   7. _____

2. _____   4. _____   6. _____   8. _____

F. Write the missing words. Use the word list.

1. The _____ was full of bees.

2. Dad put a log on the _____.

3. The owl is a _____ bird.

4. The Cubs went for a _____ on Sunday.

G. Unscramble these words. Write them.
    Find them in the wordsearch.

1. irfe   _____

2. izse   _____

3. siwe   _____

4. misle _____

5. rewi   _____

6. liave _____

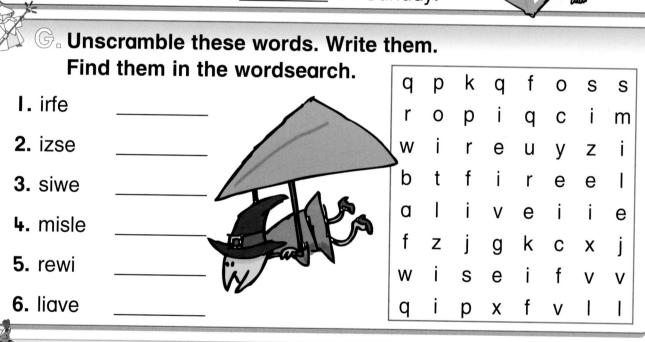

q	p	k	q	f	o	s	s
r	o	p	i	q	c	i	m
w	i	r	e	u	y	z	i
b	t	f	i	r	e	e	l
a	l	i	v	e	i	i	e
f	z	j	g	k	c	x	j
w	i	s	e	i	f	v	v
q	i	p	x	f	v	l	l

H. Colour the words that end in 'ive'.

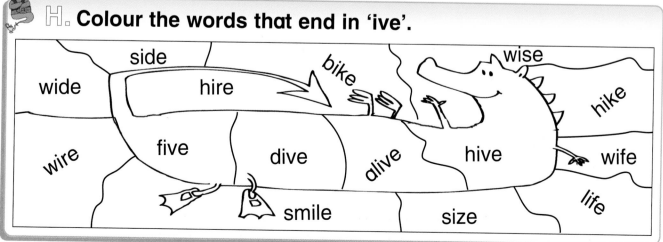

side   wise
wide   hire   bike   hike
wire   five   dive   alive   hive   wife
smile   size   life

Word List

hand ❶ foot	eye ❷ nose	head ❸ lip	ear ❹ toe
neck feet	eyes chin	hair finger	leg arm

A. Write the missing letters.

1. ha <u>n d</u>
2. __ __ ck
3. f __ __ t
4. f __ __ t

5. e __ e
6. e __ e __
7. no __ __
8. __ __ in

9. h __ __ d
10. h __ __ r
11. l __ __
12. f __ __ ger

13. ea __
14. l __ __
15. __ oe
16. __ rm

B. Write the words.

1.  *eyes*

2. _____

3. _____

4. _____

5.  _____

6. _____

7. _____

8. _____

C. Unscramble these words. Write them. Find them in the wordsearch.

1. pil   *lip*

2. yee   _____

3. ote   _____

4. ram   _____

5. gel   _____

6. are   _____

n	s	q	p	t	o	e	s
e	y	e	a	k	l	i	p
h	j	e	r	n	w	t	i
o	r	i	m	f	n	r	m
o	u	c	i	f	m	q	o
e	a	r	e	q	s	c	z
z	c	g	f	l	e	g	t
e	e	m	q	b	z	k	r

D. Write the missing words. Use the word list.

1. Tom fell and bit his ___lip___ .

2. I wear socks on my _____.

3. My _____ are blue.

4. Rudolf has a red _____.

5. Lily has long _____.

6. I have a ring on my _____.

7. I hurt my big _____.

8. My dad has hairs on his _____.

E. Write 8 words from the list using these letters. You can use a letter more than once.

o e t l g r a m i p h d n s

1. ___toe___   3. _____   5. _____   7. _____

2. _____   4. _____   6. _____   8. _____

F. Write the word. Fill in the crossword. Use the word list.

Across

2. ___feet___

3. _____

4. _____

6. _____

7. _____

Down

1. _____

2. _____

5. _____

G. Join the dots. Write the word.

1. _feet_   2. _____   3. _____   4. _____

UNIT 19

Word List

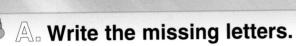

①	②	③	④
rude cube	tune June	mule pure	cure flute
nude tube	dune use	rule sure	cute duke

A. Write the missing letters.

1. r __ de
2. nu __ __
3. c __ be
4. tu __ __

5. t __ ne
6. du __ __
7. J __ ne
8. u __ e

9. m __ le
10. ru __ __
11. __ ure
12. su __ __

13. c __ re
14. cu __ __
15. fl __ te
16. d __ ke

B. Colour the correct spelling.

1. | ues | use |
2. | cube | cueb |
3. | teub | tube |

4. | rule | ruel |
5. | cuet | cute |
6. | rude | reud |

C. Match and write.

r   une
n   ute
d   re
u   ule
fl   se
pu   ude

1. _____
2. _____
3. _____
4. _____
5. _____
6. _____

D. Write the word. Colour the pictures.

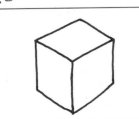   

1. _____
2. _____
3. _d_____
4. _____

E. Find 8 words in the caterpillar. Write them.

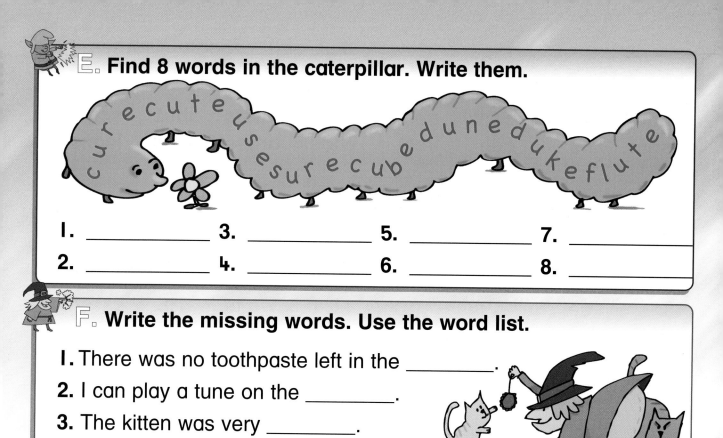

1. _____   3. _____   5. _____   7. _____

2. _____   4. _____   6. _____   8. _____

F. Write the missing words. Use the word list.

1. There was no toothpaste left in the _____.

2. I can play a tune on the _____.

3. The kitten was very _____.

4. A _____ looks a bit like a donkey.

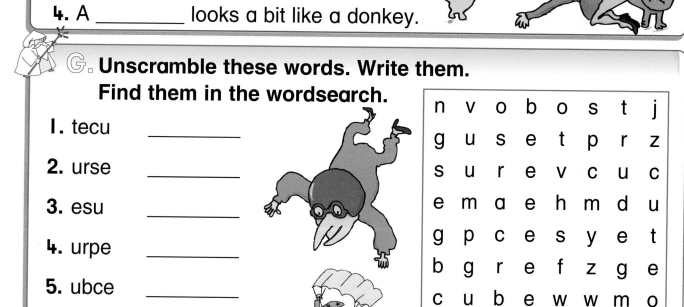

G. Unscramble these words. Write them. Find them in the wordsearch.

1. tecu   _____

2. urse   _____

3. esu   _____

4. urpe   _____

5. ubce   _____

6. udre   _____

n	v	o	b	o	s	t	j
g	u	s	e	t	p	r	z
s	u	r	e	v	c	u	c
e	m	a	e	h	m	d	u
g	p	c	e	s	y	e	t
b	g	r	e	f	z	g	e
c	u	b	e	w	w	m	o
h	c	m	p	u	r	e	i

H. Colour the words that begin with 'c'.

rude   dune   tune   tube   nude

mule   cute   June   cure   pure

cube   sure   rule

uNIT 20

Word List

hat	shoe	coat	socks	belt	boots	shirt	scarf
sock	tie	cap	vest	shoes	dress	skirt	jeans

A. Write the missing letters.

1. h __ t
2. so __ __
3. __ __ oe
4. t __ __
5. c __ __ t
6. c __ __
7. so __ __s
8. ve __ __
9. be __ __
10. __ __ oes
11. b __ __ ts
12. dr __ ss
13. sh __ __ t
14. sk __ __ t
15. __ __ ar __
16. j __ __ ns

B. Write the words.

1.  _____

2.  _____

3. _____

4. _____

5. _____

6.  _____

7. _____

8. _____

C. Unscramble these words. Write them. Find them in the wordsearch.

1. ite _____
2. toobs _____
3. oesh _____
4. toac _____
5. ssedr _____
6. neajs _____

b	i	l	y	e	k	z	h
z	s	r	m	d	b	t	x
q	s	u	x	r	o	j	f
b	h	c	f	e	o	e	b
v	o	a	o	s	t	a	v
q	e	n	u	s	s	n	m
c	o	a	t	a	e	s	g
j	a	y	t	i	e	c	e

D. Write the missing words. Use the word list.

1. Santa wears black _____.

2. My _____ keeps my neck warm.

3. I wear a _____ under my shirt.

4. The bride wore a long, white _____.

5. I got a new pair of denim _____.

6. The wind blew my _____ off my head.

7. I lost one of my woolly _____.

8. I can tie my laces on my _____.

E. Write 8 words from the list using these letters. You can use a letter more than once.

h o a t i b e l s c k p v

1. _____   3. _____   5. _____   7. _____

2. _____   4. _____   6. _____   8. _____

F. Write the word. Fill in the crossword. Use the word list.

Across

1. _____

4. _____

6. _____

7. _____

Down

1. _____

2. _____

3. _____

5. _____

G. Join the dots. Write the word.

1. _____   2. _____   3. _____   4. _____

Word List

❶	❷	❸	❹
rose nose	code bone	tore wore	hole pole
hose joke	rode cone	sore hope	sole home

A. Write the missing letters.

1. r __ se
2. ho __ __
3. n __ se
4. jo __ e

5. co __ __
6. r __ de
7. bo __ __
8. c __ ne

9. t __ re
10. so __ __
11. w __ re
12. ho __ __

13. h __ le
14. so __ __
15. p __ le
16. __ om __

B. Colour the correct spelling.

1. | roes | rose |
|---|---|

2. | joke | juke |
|---|---|

3. | beno | bone |
|---|---|

4. | wore | weor |
|---|---|

5. | hoem | home |
|---|---|

6. | code | cdeo |
|---|---|

C. Match and write.

r   ole
w   ode
h   ose
jo   ore
ho   ke
c   me

1. _____
2. _____
3. _____
4. _____
5. _____
6. _____

D. Write the word. Colour the pictures.

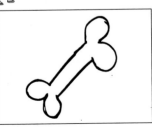

1. _____
2. _____
3. _____
4. _____

E. Find 8 words in the caterpillar. Write them.

home wore joke nose code hose tore sole

1. _____   3. _____   5. _____   7. _____

2. _____   4. _____   6. _____   8. _____

F. Write the missing words. Use the word list.

1. I _____ my new jeans to the park.

2. My friend told me a funny _____.

3. A badger's _____ is called a sett.

4. There is a _____ in the sole of my shoe.

G. Unscramble these words. Write them. Find them in the wordsearch.

1. oehp   _____

2. oecn   _____

3. oshe   _____

4. oehm   _____

5. oejk   _____

6. onbe   _____

x	p	i	n	k	l	r	i
j	w	h	o	s	e	a	u
n	b	o	n	e	u	v	h
x	s	r	c	o	n	e	o
l	a	s	m	j	j	h	m
d	w	c	i	h	o	k	e
h	o	p	e	s	k	e	d
u	e	t	x	m	e	l	c

H. Colour the words that begin with 'h'.

wore   rode   code   bone   pole   sole

hose   hole   hope   home   nose

joke   tore   cone   rose

UNIT 22

Word List

| pig | goat ❶ | lamb | foal ❷ | bull | donkey ❸ | turkey | duck ❹ |
| cow | sheep | calf | horse | hen | piglet | kid | goose |

A. Write the missing letters.

1. p __ g
2. c __ __
3. g __ __ t
4. sh __ __ p

5. la __ __
6. __ __ lf
7. f __ __ l
8. h __ __ se

9. bu __ __
10. h __ __
11. don __ __ y
12. __ __ glet

13. tur __ __ __
14. __ id
15. __ __ ck
16. g __ __ se

B. Write the words.

1. g_____

2. _____

3. _____

4. _____

5. _____

6.  _____

7. _____

8. _____

C. Unscramble these words. Write them. Find them in the wordsearch.

1. gip _____

2. oagt _____

3. loaf _____

4. ckud _____

5. segoo _____

6. keydon _____

o	g	o	a	t	u	e	c
r	p	i	g	z	t	l	z
l	y	t	s	x	k	u	o
f	o	a	l	r	d	p	h
y	a	f	u	w	u	l	c
d	u	a	q	l	c	e	h
g	o	o	s	e	k	l	e
m	d	o	n	k	e	y	x

D. Write the missing words. Use the word list.

1. A baby sheep is called a _____ .

2. The _____ has a cross on its back.

3. A baby horse is called a _____ .

4. The cow has a brown _____ .

5. The _____ had a very curly tail.

6. The Little Red _____ worked hard.

7. The _____ is on its own in the field.

8. A _____ is a baby goat.

E. Write 8 words from the list using these letters. You can use a letter more than once.

u l w t k a i d f c o p g d m b

1. _____   3. _____   5. _____   7. _____
2. _____   4. _____   6. _____   8. _____

F. Write the word. Fill in the crossword. Use the word list.

Across

1. _____

5. _____

6. f_____

7. _____

Down

1. _____

2. _____

3. _____

4. _____

G. Join the dots. Write the word.

1. _____   2. d_____   3. _____   4. _____

Word List

①		②		③		④	
sell	well	shell	hill	pill	will	full	pull
fell	bell	tell	kill	fill	drill	bull	doll

A. Write the missing letters.

1. se __ __
2. f __ ll
3. __ ell
4. b __ ll

5. sh __ ll
6. t __ ll
7. hi __ __
8. k __ ll

9. p __ ll
10. fi __ __
11. w __ ll
12. d __ ill

13. f __ ll
14. bu __ __
15. p __ ll
16. __ oll

B. Colour the correct spelling.

1. | well | wull |
4. | doll | dall |

2. | sall | sell |
5. | drull | drill |

3. | shell | sheel |
6. | kill | cill |

C. Match and write.

we   ull
s   oll
d   ill
f   ll
d   ell
b   rill

1. _____
2. _____
3. _____
4. _____
5. _____
6. _____

D. Write the word. Colour the pictures.

1. _____
2. _____
3. _____
4. _____

E. Find 8 words in the caterpillar. Write them.

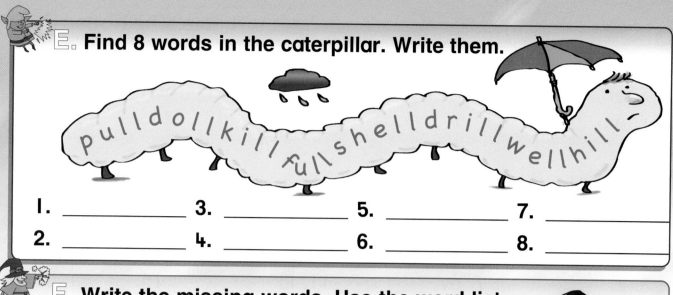

1. _____   3. _____   5. _____   7. _____

2. _____   4. _____   6. _____   8. _____

F. Write the missing words. Use the word list.

1. My _____ has black hair.

2. I found a _____ on the beach.

3. The fox fell into the _____.

4. I have a _____ on my bicycle.

G. Unscramble these words. Write them.
   Find them in the wordsearch.

1. ulbl   _____

2. ilwl   _____

3. lridl   _____

4. lold   _____

5. lilf   _____

6. hesll   _____

d	p	d	o	l	l	q	q
s	z	j	v	r	u	a	t
n	e	w	d	r	k	e	m
u	t	v	p	i	d	r	q
w	w	i	l	l	r	f	q
b	u	l	l	v	i	i	h
p	s	q	s	c	l	l	q
s	h	e	l	l	l	l	z

H. Colour the words that end in 'ell'.

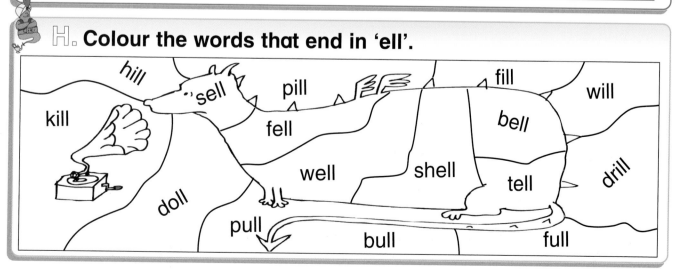

Word List

roof	❶ key	attic	❷ oven	sink	❸ lamp	hall	❹ carpet
room	floor	bed	tap	press	wall	doors	sofa

A. Write the missing letters.

1. r __ __ f
2. __ oo __
3. k __ __
4. fl __ __ r

5. a __ __ ic
6. b __ __
7. ov __ __
8. __ ap

9. si __ __
10. __ __ ess
11. la __ __
12. __ __ ll

13. ha __ __
14. d __ __ rs
15. __ __ rpet
16. so __ __

B. Write the words.

1.  _____

2.  _____

3. _____

4. _____

5.  _____

6.  _____

7.  _____

8.  _____

C. Unscramble these words. Write them. Find them in the wordsearch.

1. yek _____

2. foor _____

3. roolf _____

4. veno _____

5. pat _____

6. inks _____

u	q	x	d	z	n	h	g
k	v	o	k	w	v	w	q
j	b	o	v	e	n	w	c
k	t	w	t	j	l	r	j
a	k	k	e	y	s	o	t
f	l	o	o	r	i	o	a
f	j	v	a	z	n	f	p
c	x	m	l	j	k	c	o

D. Write the missing words. Use the word list.

1. I washed the dishes in the _____.

2. I opened the door of the _____.

3. I put the _____ in the lock.

4. We have a green _____ on our floor.

5. I sleep in a single _____.

6. The attic is under the _____.

7. I put the cake in the _____.

8. We have a wooden _____.

E. Write 8 words from the list using these letters. You can use a letter more than once.

t m v a i b y s e p d r o n f k c

1. _____   3. _____   5. _____   7. _____

2. _____   4. _____   6. _____   8. _____

F. Write the word. Fill in the crossword. Use the word list.

Across

2. _____

5. _____

6. _____

Down

1. _____

2. _____

3. _____

4. _____

G. Join the dots. Write the word.

1. _____   2. _____   3. _____   4. _____

Word List

duck	suck	back	crack	pick	kick	quick	thick
luck	sock	sack	peck	lick	flick	stick	quack

A. Write the missing letters.

1. du __ __
2. __ __ ck
3. s __ ck
4. so __ __
5. __ __ ck
6. sa __ __
7. cr __ ck
8. __ __ ck
9. p __ ck
10. __ ick
11. k __ ck
12. __ __ ick
13. qu __ __ __
14. __ ti __ __
15. th __ ck
16. qua __ __

B. Colour the correct spelling.

1.	luck	leck

4.	kick	cick

2.	dack	duck

5.	quack	qauck

3.	crack	crakc

6.	thack	thick

C. Match and write.

du   tick
s   hick
l   uack
f   ck
t   lick
q   uck

1. _____
2. _____
3. _____
4. _____
5. _____
6. _____

D. Write the word. Colour the pictures.

 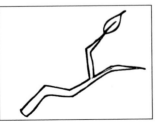  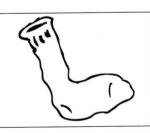

1. _____   2. _____   3. _____   4. _____

E. Find 8 words in the caterpillar. Write them.

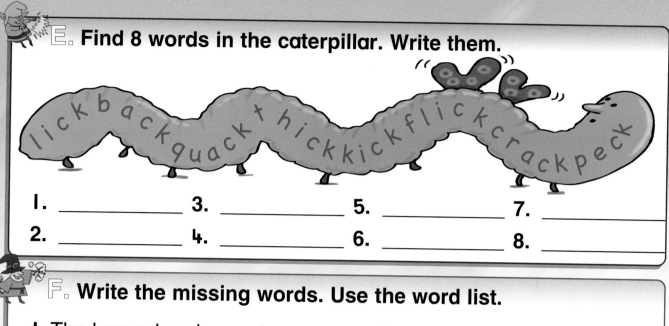

lickbackquackthickkickflickcrackpeck

1. _____   3. _____   5. _____   7. _____

2. _____   4. _____   6. _____   8. _____

F. Write the missing words. Use the word list.

1. The brown hen began to _____ the orange hen.

2. 'Quack! Quack!' said the _____.

3. Santa has a _____ of toys.

4. There is a _____ in the wall.

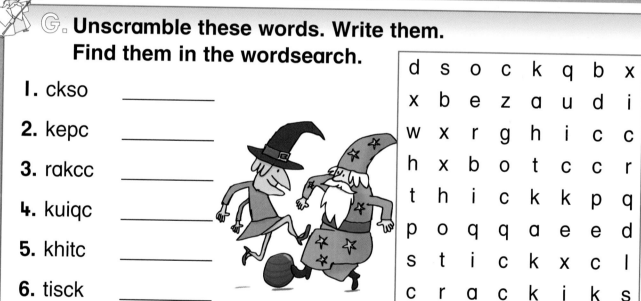

G. Unscramble these words. Write them. Find them in the wordsearch.

1. ckso   _____

2. kepc   _____

3. rakcc   _____

4. kuiqc   _____

5. khitc   _____

6. tisck   _____

d	s	o	c	k	q	b	x
x	b	e	z	a	u	d	i
w	x	r	g	h	i	c	c
h	x	b	o	t	c	c	r
t	h	i	c	k	k	p	q
p	o	q	q	a	e	e	d
s	t	i	c	k	x	c	l
c	r	a	c	k	i	k	s

H. Colour the words that begin with 's'.

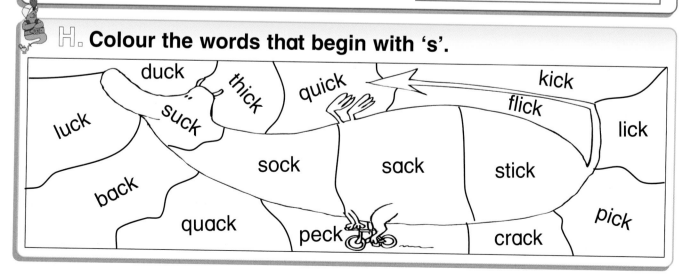

duck   thick   quick   kick   flick

luck   suck   sock   sack   stick   lick

back   quack   peck   crack   pick

Theme: Food and Drink

Word List

milk	meat	tea	soup	bread	beans	apple	peas
eggs	water	salad	banana	chips	butter	pizza	cake

A. Write the missing letters.

1. __ __ lk   5. t __ __   9. br __ __ d   13. a __ __ le

2. e __ __ s   6. s __ __ ad   10. __ __ ip __   14. pi __ __ a

3. m __ __ t   7. s __ __ p   11. b __ __ ns   15. p __ __ s

4. w __ __ er   8. b __ __ ana   12. bu __ __ er   16. c __ k __

B. Write the words.

1. _____

2. _____

3. _____

4.  _____

5. _____

6. _____

7. _____

8. _____

C. Unscramble these words. Write them.
Find them in the wordsearch.

1. pplea   _____

2. seap   _____

3. pous   _____

4. sgge   _____

5. ilmk   _____

6. team   _____

q	s	o	u	p	q	f	w
q	w	b	n	x	m	w	w
z	a	u	x	w	w	m	i
d	q	a	q	a	i	e	q
h	k	t	c	p	e	a	c
m	i	l	k	p	g	t	t
f	j	a	b	l	g	d	f
p	e	a	s	e	s	v	g

D. Write the missing words. Use the word list.

1. I like _____ and butter.

2. I take milk and sugar in my _____.

3. I eat an _____ every day.

4. My favourite _____ is lamb.

5. My dad loves tomato _____.

6. I love cheese and corn on my _____.

7. I had chocolate _____ for my birthday.

8. Our hens lay a few _____ every day.

E. Write 8 words from the list using these letters. You can use a letter more than once.

e m h i l u k c a t w r s o p

1. _____   3. _____   5. _____   7. _____

2. _____   4. _____   6. _____   8. _____

F. Write the word. Fill in the crossword. Use the word list.

Across

1. _____

3. _____

6. _____

Down

1. _____

2. _____

4. _____

5. _____

G. Join the dots. Write the word.

1. _____   2. _____   3. _____   4. _____

Word List

hay	bay	pay	lay	play	tray	stay	away
say	day	may	way	sway	pray	clay	today

A. Write the missing letters.

1. h __ __
2. __ ay
3. b __ __
4. __ ay
5. p __ y
6. m __ __
7. l __ __
8. w __ __
9. pl __ __
10. __ __ ay
11. t __ ay
12. pr __ __
13. __ __ ay
14. c __ ay
15. __ way
16. __ __ day

B. Colour the correct spelling.

1. | pray | pary |
2. | tooday | today |
3. | away | awey |
4. | saty | stay |
5. | tray | trey |
6. | clay | caly |

C. Match and write.

s   y
to   ray
s   lay
c   ay
ma   way
p   day

1. _____
2. _____
3. _____
4. _____
5. _____
6. _____

D. Write the word. Colour the pictures.

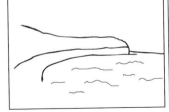
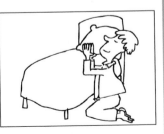

1. h _____
2. _____
3. b _____
4. _____

E. Find 8 words in the caterpillar. Write them.

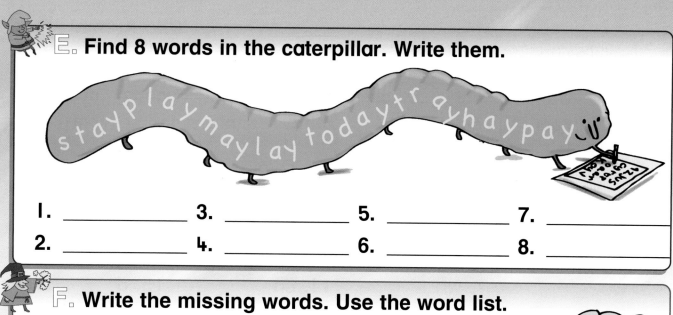

stayplaymaylaytodaytrayhaypay

1. _____   3. _____   5. _____   7. _____

2. _____   4. _____   6. _____   8. _____

F. Write the missing words. Use the word list.

1. It is very cold _____.

2. I am going to _____ with my dog.

3. We will be _____ for the weekend.

4. My cousin is coming to _____ with us.

G. Unscramble these words. Write them. Find them in the wordsearch.

1. yadto   _____

2. tays   _____

3. raty   _____

4. wasy   _____

5. rypa   _____

6. waay   _____

q	z	j	u	a	s	s	o
c	y	a	r	t	w	t	p
e	k	p	t	o	a	a	r
n	i	n	i	d	y	y	a
l	j	h	v	a	k	o	y
a	w	a	y	y	r	n	v
t	e	i	f	s	n	k	l
t	r	a	y	f	x	s	a

H. Colour the words that begin with 'p'.

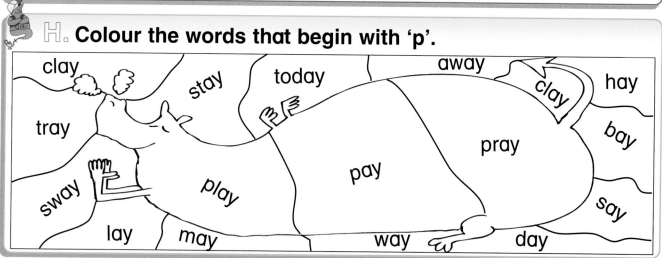

clay   stay   today   away   clay   hay

tray   sway   play   pay   pray   bay

lay   may   way   day   say

Word List

lion	① wolf	seal	② whale	monkey	③ snake	panda	④ deer
tiger	bear	camel	ape	zebra	shark	fox	bat

A. Write the missing letters.

1. l __ __ n

2. t __ __ er

3. wo __ __

4. b __ __ r

5. s __ __ l

6. c __ __ el

7. wh __ __ e

8. a __ __

9. monk __ __

10. __ __ __ ra

11. sn __ __ __ __

12. __ __ ark

13. p __ __ da

14. f __ __

15. d __ __ r

16. b __ __

B. Write the words.

1.  a _____

2.  _____

3.  _____

4.  _____

5. _____

6.  _____

7.  _____

8. _____

C. Unscramble these words. Write them. Find them in the wordsearch.

1. niol _____

2. flow _____

3. melca _____

4. tab _____

5. danpa _____

6. reed _____

f	o	i	v	w	m	f	y
f	k	p	a	n	d	a	k
r	s	s	v	z	b	d	s
m	v	h	c	y	a	e	p
c	a	m	e	l	t	e	c
w	o	l	f	a	s	r	n
x	i	o	h	r	c	l	j
a	q	l	i	o	n	l	a

D. Write the missing words. Use the word list.

1. A _____ has black and white stripes.

2. The mammy _____ is called a lioness.

3. A _____ has a bushy tail.

4. The daddy _____ is called a stag.

5. A _____ has one or two humps.

6. A _____ hangs upside down.

7. A _____ has orange and white fur.

8. A _____ has black and white fur.

E. Write 8 words from the list using these letters. You can use a letter more than once.

a f e l p i o   t n x w r s b g

1. _____   3. _____   5. _____   7. _____

2. _____   4. _____   6. _____   8. _____

F. Write the word. Fill in the crossword. Use the word list.

Across

4. _____

6. _____

7. _____

Down

1. _____

2. _____

3. _____

5. _____

G. Join the dots. Write the word.

1. _____   2. _____   3. _____   4. _____

Word List

❶	❷	❸	❹
bar far	dark card	arm farm	dart part
jar car	yard hard	alarm harm	art cart

A. Write the missing letters.

1. b__ __

2. __ ar

3. f __ r

4. c __ __

5. __ ark

6. y __ __ d

7. __ ard

8. h __ __ d

9. __ rm

10. a __ arm

11. f __ __ m

12. __ ar __

13. __ ar __

14. __ rt

15. p __ __ t

16. __ ar __

B. Colour the correct spelling.

1. | dert | dart |

2. | harm | hirm |

3. | elarm | alarm |

4. | cart | cort |

5. | purt | part |

6. | dark | derk |

C. Match and write.

d — rt
a — ar
j — ark
y — arm
f — arm
al — ard

1. _____

2. _____

3. _____

4. _____

5. _____

6. _____

D. Write the word. Colour the pictures.

      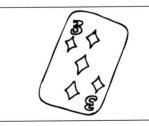   

1. _____   2. _____   3. _____   4. _____

E. Find 8 words in the caterpillar. Write them.

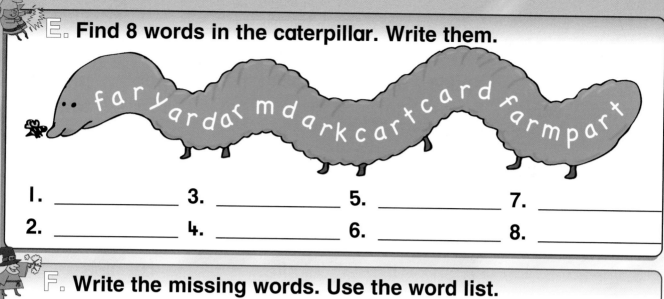

far yard arm dark cart card farm part

1. _____   3. _____   5. _____   7. _____

2. _____   4. _____   6. _____   8. _____

F. Write the missing words. Use the word list.

1. My mum drives a red _____.

2. The horse is pulling the _____.

3. I fell and hurt my _____.

4. My Uncle Tom lives on a _____.

G. Unscramble these words. Write them. Find them in the wordsearch.

1. trad   _____

2. artc   _____

3. darc   _____

4. armal _____

5. rmfa   _____

6. aprt   _____

t	p	p	e	a	j	a	k
a	l	a	r	m	c	c	h
x	n	b	f	h	a	r	t
p	a	r	t	q	r	u	f
e	z	b	i	m	d	k	a
u	l	q	k	y	c	m	r
v	k	g	j	n	i	e	m
d	a	r	t	c	a	r	t

H. Colour the words that end in 't'.

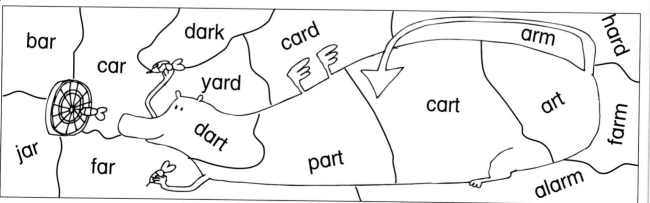

bar   dark   card   arm   hard

car   yard   cart   art

jar   dart   part   farm

far   alarm

UNIT 30

Word List

boat	sea	❶ spade	shell	❸ beach	fish	❹ pool	picnic
sand	waves	bucket	sun	crab	net	rocks	towel

A. Write the missing letters.

1. b __ __ t
2. s __ __ __
3. __ ea
4. wav __ __

5. __ __ ade
6. bu __ __ et
7. sh __ ll
8. s __ __

9. b __ __ ch
10. __ __ ab
11. fi __ __
12. n __ __

13. p __ __ l
14. ro __ __ s
15. picn __ __
16. t __ __ el

B. Write the words.

1.  _____

2.  _____

3. _____

4.  _____

5.  _____

6.  _____

7. _____

8. _____

C. Unscramble these words. Write them.
Find them in the wordsearch.

1. cheab _____
2. shif _____
3. ten _____
4. welto _____
5. nicpic _____
6. dans _____

d	n	s	f	i	s	h	s
v	e	o	u	i	h	p	a
y	t	i	g	g	b	y	n
q	i	v	p	l	e	i	d
w	t	v	g	f	a	p	r
t	o	w	e	l	c	b	z
u	c	e	l	s	h	e	h
p	i	c	n	i	c	y	l

D. Write the missing words. Use the word list.

1. We had a lovely _____ on the beach.

2. I dried myself with my _____.

3. The _____ was shining all day.

4. I found a white _____ on the sand.

5. My sister caught a _____ in her net.

6. We went for a swim in the _____.

7. A _____ tried to pinch my toe.

8. I made a sandcastle with my _____ and spade.

E. Write 8 words from the list using these letters. You can use a letter more than once.

u s b e o a k n d p t c h

1. _____   3. _____   5. _____   7. _____

2. _____   4. _____   6. _____   8. _____

F. Write the word. Fill in the crossword. Use the word list.

Across

3. _____

5. _____

6. S _____

Down

1. _____

2. _____

3. _____

4. _____

G. Join the dots. Write the word.

1. _____   2. _____   3. _____   4. _____

Word List

①		②		③		④	
sir	girl	dirt	shirt	horse	for	torn	corn
bird	stir	first	third	fork	sort	born	horn

A. Write the missing letters.

1. s __ __
2. b __ __ d
3. __ ir __
4. st __ __

5. d __ __ t
6. __ ir __ __
7. sh __ __ t
8. __ __ ir __

9. h __ __ se
10. __ or __
11. f __ __
12. __ or __

13. t __ __ n
14. __ or __
15. c __ __ n
16. __ orn

B. Colour the correct spelling.

1.	gurl	girl

2.	bird	berd

3.	furst	first

4.	borrn	born

5.	stur	stir

6.	dirt	durt

C. Match and write.

si   rk
f   rse
bi   ird
th   or
ho   r
fo   rd

1. _____
2. _____
3. _____
4. _____
5. _____
6. _____

D. Write the word. Colour the pictures.

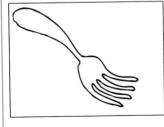   

1. _____ 2. _____ 3. _____ 4. _____

E. Find 8 words in the caterpillar. Write them.

horse torn corn fork third shirt bird sir

1. _____   3. _____   5. _____   7. _____
2. _____   4. _____   6. _____   8. _____

F. Write the missing words. Use the word list.

1. I can ride a _____.

2. Tim came _____ in the race.

3. Our dog likes to roll in the _____.

4. My baby sister was _____ on Monday.

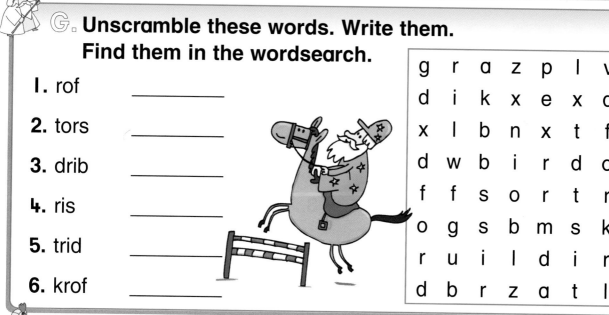

G. Unscramble these words. Write them.
Find them in the wordsearch.

1. rof   _____

2. tors   _____

3. drib   _____

4. ris   _____

5. trid   _____

6. krof   _____

g	r	a	z	p	l	v	t
d	i	k	x	e	x	d	r
x	l	b	n	x	t	f	v
d	w	b	i	r	d	o	z
f	f	s	o	r	t	r	q
o	g	s	b	m	s	k	f
r	u	i	l	d	i	r	t
d	b	r	z	a	t	l	r

H. Colour the words that begin with 's'.

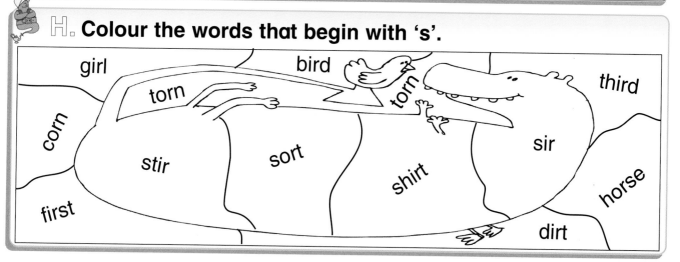

girl   bird   third

torn   torn

corn   stir   sort   shirt   sir   horse

first   dirt

UNIT 32

Word List

pen	chair	bin	copy	table	paper	ruler	shelf
bell	desk	chalk	book	paint	door	clock	chart

A. **Write the missing letters.**

1. __ en
2. be __ __
3. __ __ air
4. de __ __

5. b __ __
6. ch __ __ k
7. cop __
8. b __ __ k

9. t __ __ le
10. p __ __ nt
11. p __ __ er
12. d __ __ r

13. rul __ __
14. __ lo __ __
15. sh __ lf
16. __ __ ar __

B. **Write the words.**

1. 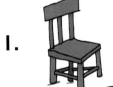 _____

2. _____

3.  _____

4. _____

5.  _____

6.  _____

7. _____

8. _____

C. **Unscramble these words. Write them.**
   Find them in the wordsearch.

1. nib _____
2. enp _____
3. lebl _____
4. raich _____
5. alkch _____
6. artch _____

b	o	f	p	c	t	m	c
f	g	b	e	h	j	c	h
b	u	u	n	a	g	t	a
o	f	j	b	l	b	k	i
r	r	c	k	k	e	v	r
c	h	a	r	t	l	w	f
n	c	b	i	n	l	d	a
h	v	d	f	a	s	c	t

D. Write the missing words. Use the word list.

1. I put the paper in the _____.
2. There was a knock on the _____.
3. I got a _____ from the library.
4. I could not find my maths _____.
5. It was one o'_____.
6. I put my book on the _____.
7. I sat on my _____.
8. My teacher has a box of white _____.

E. Write 8 words from the list using these letters. You can use a letter more than once.

k h p i y e n l b a t c r o

1. _____ 3. _____ 5. _____ 7. _____
2. _____ 4. _____ 6. _____ 8. _____

F. Write the word. Fill in the crossword. Use the word list.

Across

1. _____
5. _____
6. _____

Down

1. d_____
2. _____
3. _____
4. _____

G. Join the dots. Write the word.

1. _____ 2. _____ 3. _____ 4. _____

UNIT 1 Spelling Check

1.
2.
3.
4.
5.
6.
7.
8.
9.
10.
11.
12.
13.
14.
15.
16.

16 15 14 13 12 11 10 9 8 7 6 5 4 3 2 1

How did you do?

Excellent ☐   Good ☐
Very Good ☐   Need to Improve ☐

UNIT 2 Spelling Check

1.
2.
3.
4.
5.
6.
7.
8.
9.
10.
11.
12.
13.
14.
15.
16.

16 15 14 13 12 11 10 9 8 7 6 5 4 3 2 1

How did you do?

Excellent ☐   Good ☐
Very Good ☐   Need to Improve ☐

UNIT 3 Spelling Check

1.
2.
3.
4.
5.
6.
7.
8.
9.
10.
11.
12.
13.
14.
15.
16.

16 15 14 13 12 11 10 9 8 7 6 5 4 3 2 1

How did you do?

Excellent ☐   Good ☐
Very Good ☐   Need to Improve ☐

UNIT 4 Spelling Check

1.
2.
3.
4.
5.
6.
7.
8.
9.
10.
11.
12.
13.
14.
15.
16.

16 15 14 13 12 11 10 9 8 7 6 5 4 3 2 1

How did you do?

Excellent ☐   Good ☐
Very Good ☐   Need to Improve ☐

UNIT 5 Spelling Check

1.
2.
3.
4.
5.
6.
7.
8.
9.
10.
11.
12.
13.
14.
15.
16.

16 15 14 13 12 11 10 9 8 7 6 5 4 3 2 1

How did you do?

Excellent ☐   Good ☐
Very Good ☐   Need to Improve ☐

UNIT 6 Spelling Check

1.
2.
3.
4.
5.
6.
7.
8.
9.
10.
11.
12.
13.
14.
15.
16.

16 15 14 13 12 11 10 9 8 7 6 5 4 3 2 1

How did you do?

Excellent ☐   Good ☐
Very Good ☐   Need to Improve ☐

UNIT 7 Spelling Check

1.
2.
3.
4.
5.
6.
7.
8.
9.
10.
11.
12.
13.
14.
15.
16.

16 15 14 13 12 11 10 9 8 7 6 5 4 3 2 1

How did you do?

Excellent ☐   Good ☐
Very Good ☐   Need to Improve ☐

UNIT 8 Spelling Check

1.
2.
3.
4.
5.
6.
7.
8.
9.
10.
11.
12.
13.
14.
15.
16.

16 15 14 13 12 11 10 9 8 7 6 5 4 3 2 1

How did you do?

Excellent ☐   Good ☐
Very Good ☐   Need to Improve ☐

UNIT 9 Spelling Check

1.
2.
3.
4.
5.
6.
7.
8.
9.
10.
11.
12.
13.
14.
15.
16.

16 15 14 13 12 11 10 9 8 7 6 5 4 3 2 1

How did you do?

Excellent ☐   Good ☐

Very Good ☐   Need to Improve ☐

UNIT 10 Spelling Check

1.
2.
3.
4.
5.
6.
7.
8.
9.
10.
11.
12.
13.
14.
15.
16.

16 15 14 13 12 11 10 9 8 7 6 5 4 3 2 1

How did you do?

Excellent ☐   Good ☐

Very Good ☐   Need to Improve ☐

UNIT 11 Spelling Check

1.
2.
3.
4.
5.
6.
7.
8.
9.
10.
11.
12.
13.
14.
15.
16.

16 15 14 13 12 11 10 9 8 7 6 5 4 3 2 1

How did you do?

Excellent ☐   Good ☐

Very Good ☐   Need to Improve ☐

UNIT 12 Spelling Check

1.
2.
3.
4.
5.
6.
7.
8.
9.
10.
11.
12.
13.
14.
15.
16.

16 15 14 13 12 11 10 9 8 7 6 5 4 3 2 1

How did you do?

Excellent ☐   Good ☐

Very Good ☐   Need to Improve ☐

UNIT 13 Spelling Check

1.
2.
3.
4.
5.
6.
7.
8.
9.
10.
11.
12.
13.
14.
15.
16.

16
15
14
13
12
11
10
9
8
7
6
5
4
3
2
1

How did you do?

Excellent ☐   Good ☐
Very Good ☐   Need to Improve ☐

UNIT 14 Spelling Check

1.
2.
3.
4.
5.
6.
7.
8.
9.
10.
11.
12.
13.
14.
15.
16.

16
15
14
13
12
11
10
9
8
7
6
5
4
3
2
1

How did you do?

Excellent ☐   Good ☐
Very Good ☐   Need to Improve ☐

UNIT 15 Spelling Check

1.
2.
3.
4.
5.
6.
7.
8.
9.
10.
11.
12.
13.
14.
15.
16.

16
15
14
13
12
11
10
9
8
7
6
5
4
3
2
1

How did you do?

Excellent ☐   Good ☐
Very Good ☐   Need to Improve ☐

UNIT 16 Spelling Check

1.
2.
3.
4.
5.
6.
7.
8.
9.
10.
11.
12.
13.
14.
15.
16.

16
15
14
13
12
11
10
9
8
7
6
5
4
3
2
1

How did you do?

Excellent ☐   Good ☐
Very Good ☐   Need to Improve ☐

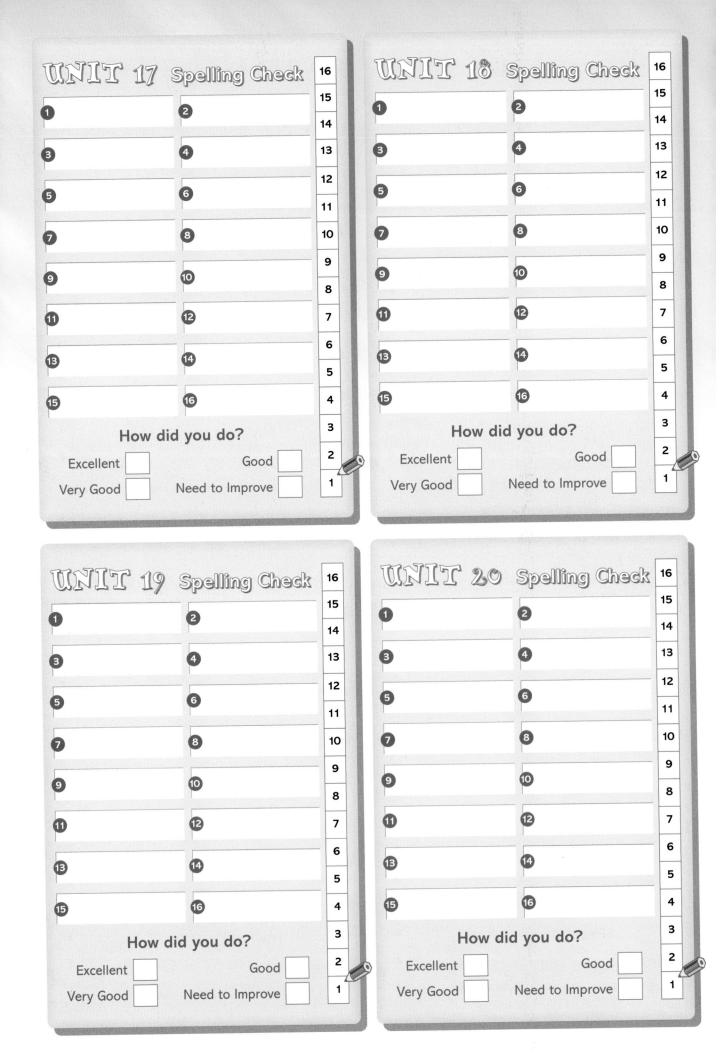

UNIT 17 Spelling Check

1.
2.
3.
4.
5.
6.
7.
8.
9.
10.
11.
12.
13.
14.
15.
16.

16 15 14 13 12 11 10 9 8 7 6 5 4 3 2 1

How did you do?

Excellent ☐   Good ☐

Very Good ☐   Need to Improve ☐

UNIT 18 Spelling Check

1.
2.
3.
4.
5.
6.
7.
8.
9.
10.
11.
12.
13.
14.
15.
16.

16 15 14 13 12 11 10 9 8 7 6 5 4 3 2 1

How did you do?

Excellent ☐   Good ☐

Very Good ☐   Need to Improve ☐

UNIT 19 Spelling Check

1.
2.
3.
4.
5.
6.
7.
8.
9.
10.
11.
12.
13.
14.
15.
16.

16 15 14 13 12 11 10 9 8 7 6 5 4 3 2 1

How did you do?

Excellent ☐   Good ☐

Very Good ☐   Need to Improve ☐

UNIT 20 Spelling Check

1.
2.
3.
4.
5.
6.
7.
8.
9.
10.
11.
12.
13.
14.
15.
16.

16 15 14 13 12 11 10 9 8 7 6 5 4 3 2 1

How did you do?

Excellent ☐   Good ☐

Very Good ☐   Need to Improve ☐

UNIT 21 Spelling Check

❶	❷	16
		15
		14
❸	❹	13
		12
❺	❻	11
❼	❽	10
		9
❾	❿	8
⓫	⓬	7
		6
⓭	⓮	5
⓯	⓰	4

How did you do?

Excellent ☐   Good ☐ | 3 |
Very Good ☐   Need to Improve ☐ | 2 |
| 1 |

UNIT 22 Spelling Check

❶	❷	16
		15
		14
❸	❹	13
		12
❺	❻	11
❼	❽	10
		9
❾	❿	8
⓫	⓬	7
		6
⓭	⓮	5
⓯	⓰	4

How did you do?

Excellent ☐   Good ☐ | 3 |
Very Good ☐   Need to Improve ☐ | 2 |
| 1 |

UNIT 23 Spelling Check

❶	❷	16
		15
		14
❸	❹	13
		12
❺	❻	11
❼	❽	10
		9
❾	❿	8
⓫	⓬	7
		6
⓭	⓮	5
⓯	⓰	4

How did you do?

Excellent ☐   Good ☐ | 3 |
Very Good ☐   Need to Improve ☐ | 2 |
| 1 |

UNIT 24 Spelling Check

❶	❷	16
		15
		14
❸	❹	13
		12
❺	❻	11
❼	❽	10
		9
❾	❿	8
⓫	⓬	7
		6
⓭	⓮	5
⓯	⓰	4

How did you do?

Excellent ☐   Good ☐ | 3 |
Very Good ☐   Need to Improve ☐ | 2 |
| 1 |

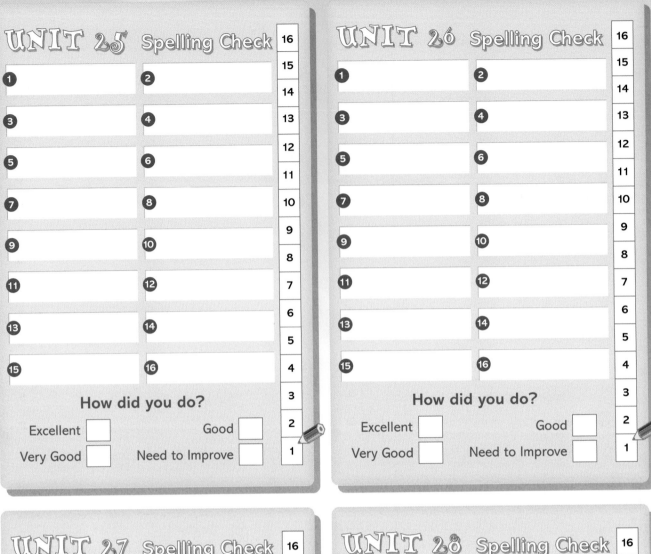

UNIT 25 Spelling Check

1
2
3
4
5
6
7
8
9
10
11
12
13
14
15
16

16
15
14
13
12
11
10
9
8
7
6
5
4
3
2
1

How did you do?

Excellent

Good

Very Good

Need to Improve

UNIT 26 Spelling Check

1
2
3
4
5
6
7
8
9
10
11
12
13
14
15
16

16
15
14
13
12
11
10
9
8
7
6
5
4
3
2
1

How did you do?

Excellent

Good

Very Good

Need to Improve

UNIT 27 Spelling Check

1
2
3
4
5
6
7
8
9
10
11
12
13
14
15
16

16
15
14
13
12
11
10
9
8
7
6
5
4
3
2
1

How did you do?

Excellent

Good

Very Good

Need to Improve

UNIT 28 Spelling Check

1
2
3
4
5
6
7
8
9
10
11
12
13
14
15
16

16
15
14
13
12
11
10
9
8
7
6
5
4
3
2
1

How did you do?

Excellent

Good

Very Good

Need to Improve

UNIT 29 Spelling Check

1.
2.
3.
4.
5.
6.
7.
8.
9.
10.
11.
12.
13.
14.
15.
16.

16 15 14 13 12 11 10 9 8 7 6 5 4 3 2 1

How did you do?

Excellent ☐   Good ☐
Very Good ☐   Need to Improve ☐

UNIT 30 Spelling Check

1.
2.
3.
4.
5.
6.
7.
8.
9.
10.
11.
12.
13.
14.
15.
16.

16 15 14 13 12 11 10 9 8 7 6 5 4 3 2 1

How did you do?

Excellent ☐   Good ☐
Very Good ☐   Need to Improve ☐

UNIT 31 Spelling Check

1.
2.
3.
4.
5.
6.
7.
8.
9.
10.
11.
12.
13.
14.
15.
16.

16 15 14 13 12 11 10 9 8 7 6 5 4 3 2 1

How did you do?

Excellent ☐   Good ☐
Very Good ☐   Need to Improve ☐

UNIT 32 Spelling Check

1.
2.
3.
4.
5.
6.
7.
8.
9.
10.
11.
12.
13.
14.
15.
16.

16 15 14 13 12 11 10 9 8 7 6 5 4 3 2 1

How did you do?

Excellent ☐   Good ☐
Very Good ☐   Need to Improve ☐

HALLOWE'EN Spelling Check

1.

2.

3.

4.

5.

6.

7.

8.

9.

10.

11.

12.

13.

14.

15.

16.

Based on
Units done
up to:

Hallowe'en

16
15
14
13
12
11
10
9
8
7
6
5
4
3
2
1

How did you do?

Excellent ☐   Good ☐

Very Good ☐   Need to Improve ☐

CHRISTMAS Spelling Check

1.

2.

3.

4.

5.

6.

7.

8.

9.

10.

11.

12.

13.

14.

15.

16.

Based on
Units done
up to:

Christmas

16
15
14
13
12
11
10
9
8
7
6
5
4
3
2
1

How did you do?

Excellent ☐   Good ☐

Very Good ☐   Need to Improve ☐

EASTER Spelling Check

1.
2.
3.
4.
5.
6.
7.
8.
9.
10.
11.
12.
13.
14.
15.
16.

Based on Units done up to:

Easter

16
15
14
13
12
11
10
9
8
7
6
5
4
3
2
1

How did you do?

Excellent [ ]   Good [ ]

Very Good [ ]   Need to Improve [ ]

SUMMER Spelling Check

1.
2.
3.
4.
5.
6.
7.
8.
9.
10.
11.
12.
13.
14.
15.
16.

Based on Units done up to:

Summer

16
15
14
13
12
11
10
9
8
7
6
5
4
3
2
1

How did you do?

Excellent [ ]   Good [ ]

Very Good [ ]   Need to Improve [ ]

Unit 1	Unit 2	Unit 3	Unit 4	Unit 5
is	pan	lap	up	fix
it	ran	nap	we	fit
in	van	cap	am	hit
to	has	gap	at	bit
go	hat	bat	be	dip
me	rat	mat	do	hip
my	sat	fat	he	pig
see	pat	bag	no	dig
the	tap	jam	on	big
run	map	dam	got	mix
red	rap	bad	get	him
not	ham	dad	did	his
for	rag	can	but	hid
can	sad	fan	you	did
big	mad	tan	all	fin
and	had	man	are	bin

Unit 6	Unit 7	Unit 8	Unit 9	Unit 10
kid	ten	rot	nut	wag
lid	men	dot	but	flag
sit	den	got	put	stag
pit	hen	pot	hut	drag
lit	pet	cot	fun	clap
win	vet	bob	bun	trap
tin	wet	rob	sun	flap
pin	jet	rod	gun	ram
rib	get	cod	rug	chat
bib	net	pod	dug	flat
rip	red	dog	hug	plan
lip	fed	fog	mug	than
pip	bed	jog	tug	that
tip	leg	bog	mud	ant
wig	web	fox	cup	have
six	yes	box	cut	glad

Complete Word List

Unit 11	Unit 12	Unit 13	Unit 14	Unit 15
zip	set	on	rub	cake
whip	met	not	tub	rake
ship	peg	hot	run	take
skip	less	lot	nun	care
trip	mess	log	jug	late
with	dress	blob	bug	gate
miss	press	moss	plug	date
kiss	bless	toss	slug	fade
ink	best	top	dust	same
pink	nest	mop	rust	name
think	rest	shot	trust	case
this	test	trot	bus	made
still	then	shop	bud	cane
milk	when	stop	sum	lane
twig	upset	flop	shut	mane
slid	forget	drop	club	face

Unit 16	Unit 17	Unit 18	Unit 19	Unit 20
file	wide	hand	rude	hat
mile	side	neck	nude	sock
pile	hike	foot	cube	shoe
tile	bike	feet	tube	tie
pipe	five	eye	tune	coat
ripe	dive	eyes	dune	cap
ride	hive	nose	June	socks
tide	alive	chin	use	vest
wine	fire	head	mule	belt
fine	wire	hair	rule	shoes
bite	hire	lip	pure	boots
kite	wise	finger	sure	dress
hide	wife	ear	cure	shirt
pine	life	leg	cute	skirt
like	smile	toe	flute	scarf
time	size	arm	duke	jeans

79

Unit 21	Unit 22	Unit 23	Unit 24	Unit 25	Unit 26
rose	pig	sell	roof	duck	milk
hose	cow	fell	room	luck	eggs
nose	goat	well	key	suck	meat
joke	sheep	bell	floor	sock	water
code	lamb	shell	attic	back	tea
rode	calf	tell	bed	sack	salad
bone	foal	hill	oven	crack	soup
cone	horse	kill	tap	peck	banana
tore	bull	pill	sink	pick	bread
sore	hen	fill	press	lick	chips
wore	donkey	will	lamp	kick	beans
hope	piglet	drill	wall	flick	butter
hole	turkey	full	hall	quick	apple
sole	kid	bull	doors	stick	pizza
pole	duck	pull	carpet	thick	peas
home	goose	doll	sofa	quack	cake

Unit 27	Unit 28	Unit 29	Unit 30	Unit 31	Unit 32
hay	lion	bar	boat	sir	pen
say	tiger	jar	sand	bird	bell
bay	wolf	far	sea	girl	chair
day	bear	car	waves	stir	desk
pay	seal	dark	spade	dirt	bin
may	camel	yard	bucket	first	chalk
lay	whale	card	shell	shirt	copy
way	ape	hard	sun	third	book
play	monkey	arm	beach	horse	table
sway	zebra	alarm	crab	fork	paint
tray	snake	farm	fish	for	paper
pray	shark	harm	net	sort	door
stay	panda	dart	pool	torn	ruler
clay	fox	art	rocks	born	clock
away	deer	part	picnic	corn	shelf
today	bat	cart	towel	horn	chart